EVEN LAME DUCKS CAN SOAR

An inspiring story of revival based on ancient wisdoms, scientific facts & divine promises.

Patricia Dunican

Clara Vale Publishing

Dedication

In loving memory of my parents,
Jim and Molly (née Carroll)
whose home was always a sanctuary for lame ducks.

Table of Contents

INTRODUCTION

We were the most unlikely twins. We didn't even have the same birthday. I slid effortlessly into the world at twenty three minutes before midnight on the 15th of March, Lucy arrived in distress, and struggling for breath, in the first minutes of the 16th. This set the pattern for her existence. Nothing came easy. She was academically weak, physically frail, and susceptible to any virus or infection that was going. Her eyesight was poor and her hearing less than perfect. Her hands and feet were always cold. Her wispy blonde hair framed her pale little face, and sometimes, just for an instant, her wide eyes seemed to lose focus and look past you into another world.

I was tall, strong, and as healthy as a trout. With my ruddy cheeks and dark unruly curls I was the image of my father's mother, or so I was constantly told, although, as far as I could see, there was absolutely no resemblance between me and the warm, rotund, white haired granny whom I loved.

From the start I looked out for Lucy. We all did. Her vulnerability brought out the best in all those whose lives she touched. In school I'd take off her shoes and rub her icy feet while she massaged her numb, frozen fingers, until the feeling returned to them. Then we'd sit close together in one of the big wooden desks.

We shared most things; the same bedroom, toys, and friends. They were my friends really. Lucy didn't make friends. She didn't need anyone else but me. She was happy as long as we were together. I was her hero. She took her lead from me. Sometimes that annoyed me. Sometimes I'd complain that she was copying me and that I could never go anywhere without her. Sometimes I wished to escape from her. But in truth those occasions were rare. I loved Lucy. And more importantly Lucy loved me. She quoted me all the time. It was always; "Rachael does it like this," and "Rachael said so." That made me feel so good.

1

When we finished in secondary school she went to help in our neighbour's garden centre and loved working there. I continued with my education, eventually graduating as a doctor. Lucy was in no small way responsible for my choice of career. I wanted to see if there was any way that I could help make her feel better, cure her allergies, or help relieve the headaches she often complained of.

On Saturday April 6th 2013, three weeks after her thirty second birthday, Lucy died. I cannot describe my pain. But for my parents' sake I continued on, keeping up appearances, while all the while drawing closer to the edge. Then one day the inevitable happened; the truth seeped out through the cracks in my veneer, and my life fell apart. This is the story of how I learned to put it together again, in the company of the other lame ducks attending Tara's Good Vibrations course.

PANIC

I knew I was tempting fate by going into the supermarket in Mullingar, but it wasn't as big a risk as shopping in the village. The last few times I had gone into Byrne's I had had to abandon my basket of groceries and escape to the car when someone sympathised with me about Lucy.

I couldn't bear to think of her. The consequences were too severe. Every time she came to mind I pushed her away. The image of her, in her favourite green dress, lying cold, lonely, and frightened, in that box deep down in the dark earth was unbearable. It was her first time away from home. She'd be terrified without me. She was afraid of the dark. I could imagine her putting her tiny, limp hand on her heart, stammering, and gasping for breath, as she always did when she was afraid or under stress.

At the thought of her distress my own body would also go into terror mode. It was as if I became possessed of demons that tried to strangle, terrify, and shake the life out of me too. My heart would thump, my stomach lurch, and no matter how hard I tried I couldn't catch a breath. This feeling conjured up memories of another devastating period in my life; another time when my panic was indescribable.

Each unsuccessful attempt to breathe fed the fear that I was going to suffocate and die. The gasping, panicking, and terror became a vicious circle which continued until I was totally exhausted and completely depleted of energy and confidence. I knew I was on the edge. I didn't know how much longer I could continue like that. But I had to try. I couldn't fall apart. I was supposed to be the strong one. I had to keep going, to keep up the pretence, to continue as normal.

I parked in Dunne's Store's car park half an hour before closing time and observed the people going in and coming out. When I was almost certain that the store was empty I walked in briskly, grabbed a basket and practically ran down the main aisle, snatching the most conveniently placed food items at random; a tin of beans, a packet of soup, a loaf of bread; just enough to keep body and soul together.

I was at the fridge when a hand touched me gently on the arm and I looked into the sad face of Ronnie Maher, a friend from primary school. No words were necessary. She hugged me tightly. I nodded my appreciation, and with all the strength I could muster turned and lurched with tear filled eyes towards the door. I felt as if I was about to vomit. I had to get out. I absolutely had to get out. I needed air. I needed to breathe. I needed to get to the car, to get home to safety.

Panicking I staggered along. Reeling towards the main door I collided with someone coming out of one of the side aisles. The basket fell from my grip scattering its contents all over the floor, but I continued on; my attention on the exit sign. While I was aware of a woman's presence beside me, and could hear her voice, "Bray," was the only word which registered with me as I stumbled towards the door. To add to my discomfort she hurried along with me to the car, which, thankfully, I had parked as near to the shop as possible.

"Rachael, are you alright? Can I help you?" she asked as I leaned against it trying to steady myself.

"No thank you. I'm fine," I stammered, my shaking body betraying my true state. When my trembling hand finally held steady long enough for me to open the door I sat down on the driver's seat and closed my eyes to shut out the pain.

"It's me Rachael," she said hunkering down as you would to speak to a child. I recognised the voice but couldn't place it.

"It's Tara. Tara Arnould. I am so sorry about Lucy."

I didn't hear anything else. I couldn't bear to. She put something in my hand just before I closed the car door and sobbed my heart out. When I could muster up the energy I drove home very carefully.

In the blessed silence, dark, and privacy of my home, negotiating by the light of the street lamp, I collapsed into the chair nearest the door and closed my eyes. But, despite feeling exhausted, I made a conscious effort not to sleep. Sleep brought its own terror. Since Lucy's death my dreams were populated by zombies, who, in their living dead state, sought to torment me for failing to cure their ills.

I did fall asleep however, because a few hours later I woke from a terrifying dream, covered in sweat, with tears rolling down my cheeks, and with my heart beating so fast that I stayed completely still for fear any extra exertion would cause it to explode. This latest nightmare was staged in a church during a funeral. I knew it was a funeral, although no coffin was visible. The scene was black and sombre. The window-less walls were covered in heavy cobwebs. The congregation wore hooded, long black robes. Even the floor was covered in black carpet. Well it looked like carpet, but as soon as I stepped on it, it moved. I realised then, that it was in fact a sea of fat black worms. They swept me off my feet, and carried me along as on a wave, until I crashed with great force onto the highest step of the altar. Leaning on my hands I made many unsuccessful attempts to get up, but the worms kept moving, making that impossible.

Eventually they slid over me, covering me completely. I had the sensation of smothering, but was unable to scream for help since they would then come into my mouth and take possession of my body. Finally I stopped struggling, and as if by a miracle found myself facing the congregation. Silently they started to move as one, gliding out of their seats and coming forward heads bowed to form a long black line. As each one drew level with me it lifted its head causing the hood of the robe to fall backwards, revealing a skull. Pausing for a moment, each pair of angry eyes glared at me. In those eyes I recognised the essence of some of my patients, both past and present.

Each in turn pointed a skeletal finger threateningly at me before disintegrating into a pile of black dust. I tried to escape from what seemed like an endless queue of zombies making their way towards me, but could see no way out. Later they became more aggressive, reaching out and pulling at my hair and clothing.

Then Lucy stood in front of me. Beautiful, smiling, gentle Lucy, my adoring and adorable sister. She rose up on her tippy toes, wrapped her thin arms around my neck, and hugged me tightly.

"Let's go home Lucy," I said taking her by the hand. She didn't move. "Come on Lucy," I begged in the voice I always used to cajole her.

But she still didn't budge. It was as if she was stuck to the spot. Hard as I tried, I was no match for the invisible power which wrestled her hand from my grip and spirited her away from me as quickly as she had come.

"Lucy," I screamed frantically, over and over again. But all that came back to me was an echo. Guilt, grief, terror, heartache caused me to pass out.

When I awoke, gasping for breath, I finally admitted defeat. I couldn't take any more. I was physically, mentally, and emotionally drained. I had to get away. I just had to get away. I needed time to consider what to do next.

At 7.30 a.m. I rang the surgery. Trying to sound as normal as possible I asked Mary to put me through to Dr. Steven's Office.

"Good morning Rachael," his voice as ever was strong and confident; the same tone he had used to assured me that there was nothing more that anyone could have done to save Lucy's life. That no matter how many tests had been conducted on her, the brain tumour, because of its location, would have remained undetected.

"How can I help you?" he asked.

I tried to compose myself. Yet again the mere thought of Lucy disturbed me deeply. Would I ever again find peace? I wondered. This unbearable thought caused the tears to well up. Desperately trying to conceal my emotions I let the words tumble out, not having the presence of mind, or the energy, to censor them in any way.

"I know it's very short notice," I stumbled, "but something extremely important of a personal nature has come up and I need time to try to sort it out. I believe it's in the best interests of the practice that I give this matter my full attention. I feel that I wouldn't be able to operate as efficiently as I should if my energies were divided. If this makes things difficult for you then I'll certainly go in, but I would prefer if I could take some time off with immediate effect."

I knew that I was rattling on, talking too fast, babbling, but I just had to get the words out while I could still speak. I held my breath waiting for his response as my heart thumped and I could feel my temperature rising. After what seemed like an age, but was probably just a matter of seconds, he replied.

"Of course Rachael, I understand. I know it must be very urgent for you to take time out. I trust the matter is resolved to your satisfaction very soon." Then he added enigmatically; "Remember Rachael, I consider you a friend as well as a colleague, so if I can help in any way please don't hesitate to contact me. It's no shame to ask for help. There comes a time in all our lives when the going gets tough. Take care of yourself and let me know how you are doing."

That was the final straw. The tears started to flow and I just managed to croak out a very weak, "Thank you," before they became a torrent. Dr. Steven was a wise old owl and had no doubt realised that I was under extreme pressure. For the past few weeks, since Lucy's death in fact, every time I met him I was looking for reassurance. There was always a "what if" question. What if I hadn't accepted her doctor's view that the headaches which plagued her were related to her proven allergies? What if I had insisted on further tests? What if I had strongly recommended that she consult a brain surgeon? What if I had taken more time to listen to her? What if? What if?

Of course he knew that I was devastated at the loss of my sister, but did he realise that my problem was more deep-seated than that? That it had been building for some years, since shortly after qualification in fact. And that it had grown incrementally over time as the number of patients presenting with conditions they had presented with years previously had continued to increase. I was certain that was not the way it should be. In the very recent past this situation had started to seriously impact on my peace of mind. I dreaded each morning facing another day meeting people who were depending on me for help; help which, in some cases, I was unable to give.

And then Lucy died. Her death had been the final straw. She was my twin sister. I knew that she was delicate, but I had failed her. I was a doctor. I was supposed to help sick people, and yet the person I loved most in the whole world had died and I had been of no assistance to her. Added to this there was another, more selfish reason for my distress. I was now faced with the harsh reality that I too was vulnerable. Before Lucy's death I had felt confident in my health, in my life and future. Looking forward the horizon had always seemed a long distance away. Lucy's death had changed all that. Nothing was certain anymore. I had become anxious, forgetful, and ill at ease. Of course Dr. Steven had noticed, but I didn't have the energy to worry about that now. Now I had to concentrate all my efforts on getting well.

I went into the kitchen and made a pot of coffee. Half a loaf of bread was all the food I had in the house. I put two slices in the toaster and reckoned that the remainder would be sufficient for the rest of the day. I couldn't bear the thought of going out to the shop. I didn't want to meet anyone.

The ringing of the doorbell startled me. Peeping through the curtains I saw that it was Joanne. I had no intention of answering it. Joanne was a wonderful neighbour, very caring and concerned, but also very astute. I didn't want her to see me in my present state. But when the ringing persisted I surrendered.

"Oh thank goodness you're alright Rachael," she said with visible relief. "I was worried about you. There was a break-in on the road last night. When I saw that your car hadn't been moved this morning I was concerned. You can never be too careful when people are living alone. We'll all have to be more vigilant from now on."

I didn't enquire which house had been burgled, or whether anyone had been injured. I just wanted to get rid of Joanne as soon as possible. So in the brightest voice I could muster I replied. "Thank you so much for your concern Joanne, but as you can see, I'm perfect. In fact I'm on holiday at the moment, that's why the car hasn't moved yet."

I don't know where the idea came from, but I was then prompted to add; "Actually I'm going away for a little while. It's been ages since I had a holiday."

"That's right," she interrupted. "You haven't been away in three years. It will do you good. We all need a change to recharge the batteries. It will help you heal."

I gave her a big smile before closing the door.

"What did you say that for?" I berated myself in the hall. "Now what are you going to do? You'll have to go somewhere. She'll be watching you. Where are you going to go, on you own, in your condition?"

Then a gentle voice whispered "Bray".

Bray is a seaside town about 20 kilometres, (12 miles) south of Dublin, Ireland's capital city. Pre budget-airlines it was where many Irish families, including ours, went for their summer break. Every year, for twelve years in a row, we had holidayed in a little house off Strand Road. For us, a family from an inland town, it was a magical place. The house belonged to Jim Leahy, my father's childhood friend. Jim worked in the Civil Service in Dublin and had settled down in Bray. My father and he had a gentleman's agreement. Every summer they swopped homes for two weeks. This arrangement suited all concerned. Jim's family got to visit their granny without his wife, Joan, having to spend too much time under her mother-in-law's roof, and we got to enjoy two fabulous weeks by the seaside.

Within a few minutes walking distance of Jim's house was everything a child could wish for. The stretch of green grass between the road and the strand was where we played football and had our picnics. We walked our terrier, Eddie, along the promenade which stretched from the small harbour to the foot of Bray Head, and we swam, made sand castles, tumbled and played on the beach. All the cash we collected during the year, any birthday, communion, or confirmation money, we squirreled away to spend with reckless abandon in the little kiosks which sold sand buckets and spades, ice cream and candy floss, all along the promenade. They were exotic looking structures, tiny circular buildings with turrets like pictures in fairy stories.

At nightfall the whole area assumed another atmosphere, changing from a child's paradise to a place where love stories began, or continued. The little fairy lights, which ran the length of the promenade, lit up. Local groups and on special occasions, national bands set up their instruments on the bandstand, and when the music began happy holi-day-makers danced the night away. It was fantastic. At midnight we'd go home to bed, always smiling it seemed.

Initially we travelled by train, but in later years, when my father got promotion and a car, we had access not only to Bray, but to the beautiful countryside around it. We'd visit Dalkey, Killiney, Greystones, the village of Enniskerry and the monastic settlement of Glendalough.

Then, of course, we grew up and weren't interested in playing on the beach, or picnicking on the grass, or climbing Bray Head. All those activities became "boring." And so our holidays in Bray came to an end. It had been nearly sixteen years since I had last been there. Now it seemed that circumstances beyond my control were conspiring to bring me back again. I was willing to discover why.

The next morning, after another night of fitful sleep, I woke relieved to find that I was not actually drowning; that the water, which was cascading down the walls of the house and filling the sitting room where I was trapped, was only in my dream.

In the kitchen there was one slice of bread left, but that was enough. I didn't feel hungry. It was 7 a.m. If I hurried I could make my escape when Joanne left on her school run.

With my bag containing a few pairs of slacks, tops, underwear and toiletries, I set off as soon as she had exited the estate. When I opened the car door a piece of card lying on the floor caught my eye. Lifting it up I read: Tara Arnould, Energy Therapist, Harbour View, Bray, County Wicklow.

During the past few years I had sometimes wondered what had become of Tara Arnould. As young teenagers we had attended the same secondary school for a very short time. She was one of the "in set", invited to all the birthday parties, chosen for the sports teams, much favoured by the teaching staff, some of whom played golf with her parents. At that stage, from my point of view, she led a charmed life. The Arnould family was very wealthy, well connected, and powerful. Her father Claud, managing director of the largest fertilizer producing factory in the country, was the biggest employer in the area. The social columns invariable made flattering references to the latest party at the "Le Lavandou Stud", or carried a photograph of Mr. and Mrs. Arnould attending some charity dinner or other. Then the house of Arnould came tumbling down.

It was at this time that Tara had presented at the surgery. She was very ill and totally unrecognisable from the Tara whose engagement photo I had recently seen in the pages of the local paper. Her unkempt, debilitated appearance had shocked me. She was undernourished, dehydrated, and severely depressed. Her clothes hung from her shoulders and she was so frail that she had difficulty walking. Her accompanying friend had outlined the series of disasters which had brought her to this point, confirming the truth of the rumours which had spread like wildfire through the county.

The image of her leaving the surgery, supported by her companion, stayed with me for some time. It was a pitiful sight. Not for the first time in my career I felt that my prescription for antidepressants was inadequate.

I later heard that she had left Mullingar and had gone to live with her paternal grandmother in France. But, wherever she had been, she was now back in Ireland, and while I hadn't been able to see her that night in the supermarket car park, she was obviously in a much better place than she had been five years previously. I wondered how she had done it.

It was practically all dual carriageway to Bray. A fantastic piece of engineering had replaced the narrow winding road we had travelled in my father's old Ford Cortina. But it was soulless. I bypassed all the little towns we used to drive through; Kilbeggan, Kinnegad, where we'd stop for ice-cream, Kilcock, Maynooth, then over the Liffey at Leixlip, and on into Dublin city. Once we saw the canal we knew that we were nearly there. By contrast my trip was uninteresting, just miles and miles of motorway.

The town of Bray is situated on the River Dargle which flows from the majestic Wicklow Mountains to its west. On my arrival I turned left at the first set of traffic lights after the bridge. From there I followed the river to our mutual destination, the Irish Sea.

On first sight it was obvious that Strand Road hadn't changed much. The large Victorian houses still stood as sentinels; solid and strong, shoulder to shoulder, defending the town from attack by the sea. Indeed their strength had often been tested by the gale force easterly winds and the mighty waves which they powered.

I noticed that some had been turned into nursing homes. A few blocks of apartments had also been added since I was last there. But there was no doubting that this was still the Bray of my childhood. The kiosks were newly painted in preparation for the summer season. The chippers still wafted out their irresistible smell. Most of the people sitting on the low wall opposite the amusement arcade had succumbed to their temptation, happily munching out of brown paper bags.

Beach Terrace was still standing. I had to steel myself not to cry as I drove past the house where we had stayed when the whole family was still intact, and where we were happy. Then panic struck, the feeling of dread hit me, and I pulled up at the first hotel I encountered unable to drive any further.

The Promenade Hotel was a different colour to what I remembered it to be, but that seemed to be the only difference from those times when our parents used go there for a drink, and we'd have a treat; a glass of fizzy orange. This memory exacerbated my feelings of sadness and unease. I could feel my stomach tighten and my breath become shallow. I started to panic. I had to retreat from the world. I had to get in somewhere, anywhere. I needed to rest.

"How long will you be staying?" the receptionist asked.

"I'm not sure, a couple of days," I managed to say as I took the key and hurried towards the lift.

In the room I collapsed onto the bed and slept for a few hours. When I awoke it was still bright. From my window I could see the people walking, laughing, swimming, sailing, picnicking and generally enjoying themselves in the great outdoors, while I was dreading the thought of having to go out to the car to fetch my luggage. When I eventually retrieved it and returned to the room, I psyched myself up and called home.

"It's me Mam," I said in response to the barely recognisable voice which answered after a long ringing session. "It's Rachael," I added. "How are you today?"

"Fine Rachael. We're fine." Again the expression-less voice replaced the melodic enthusiastic one I was familiar with.

"Where's Dad."

"He's out around the place somewhere."

"How's he doing?"

"Fine Rachael."

"You'll never guess where I am," I blurted out in an effort to infuse a little life into the conversation. As soon as I said it I regretted it. The mention of Bray would surely only make matters worse.

"No," came the reply and I knew that what I had said hadn't even registered with her. So I added casually, "I've decided to take a holiday Mam. I need a break. But don't worry about me. I'm fine."

"That's good Rachael. Take care of yourself," she said before hanging up.

Then I lay down on the bed and cried. Things were so different without Lucy. While she was there her love and need for me had ensured that I was an important member of the family. Without her, the perpetual child, it seemed as if I was redundant. Once again I felt overcome with grief and so alone. Was this the way it was going to be? I wasn't ready to contemplate the answer to that question so I turned on the television for company, lay down on the bed once more and fell into a disturbed and fitful sleep.

At 3 a.m. I woke just as the walking dead were closing in on me. But this time there was no escaping them. They had invaded the room.

13

Huge shapes, now dark, now bright, towered over me. Everything was distorted. I was terrified and sneaked down under the bedclothes, afraid to breathe. After some time, on the point of smothering, I peeped out very cautiously to discover that my monsters were generated by the flickering light of the television as it played silently in the dark.

As usual I was watching for daylight. When the first rays of the sun rose above the horizon I got up, made a cup of tea and forced down one of the plain biscuits from the packet which was on the tray beside the kettle. Then I showered, dressed, and not wanting to speak to anyone, left the room before the cleaners came. Scuttling across the road I sat down in the ornamental shelter facing the sea. It was a place which my mother loved. I wondered if she would ever recover enough to enjoy anything again. I couldn't imagine her throwing back her head and laughing heartily as she used to. I couldn't imagine me ever laughing in that way either, not the way I did when we were there on that same beach years previously. My mind would have continued to travel backwards but for a cheery greeting which returned me to the present.

"Hi Rachael, welcome to Bray. We'll have to stop meeting like this," Tara Arnould said, sitting down on the stone seat beside me.

Even up close and in full daylight she looked stunning. I marvelled that anyone could look so well, so calm and composed, after what she had been through. There was a glow about her as if she was lit from within. Her olive skin was lightly tanned, her chestnut hair shone, and her hazel eyes were bright and smiling.

"I didn't expect to see you so soon again. Twice in the space of a few days, after a seventeen year gap!" she said, either having no memory of our meeting in the surgery, or not wishing to recall it.

"Isn't it lovely?" she asked, motioning to the sea and the surrounding area. "If you're free, perhaps you'd like to join me. I'm going on the cliff walk. You'll love it. It's spectacular," she said, referring to the pedestrian walk which hugs the eastern side of Bray Head, and overlooks the sea all the way to the little fishing village of Greystones, about seven kilometres, (four miles) further south along the coast. On a clear

14

day it affords stunning views of Dublin Bay. In a glance, one can span an area of eighty kilometres. (fifty miles) Wicklow Head, Killiney, Dalkey, Ringsend, to the south of the city and Clontarf, and Howth on the north side are all visible. As a family we had often walked along by the cliffs carrying our sandwiches, which we then ate with a hearty appetite on the beach in Greystones.

"We'll be back in time for lunch," she added by way of encouragement.

"Not today thank you; perhaps another time," I replied knowing that I couldn't possibly walk seven kilometres. This realisation only served to add to my distress. I had walked most of the long-distance hiking trails in Ireland and Britain, and now I felt unable to complete a walk which any child could comfortably manage.

"That's a pity. Perhaps before you go home. Are you staying long in Bray?" she asked getting up and preparing to continue on.

"Just a few days," I replied, suddenly realising that I hadn't given that any consideration. I had just needed to escape.

"If you're still here on Tuesday I'd love you to come to my course in the community centre. You might find it interesting," she said handing me her card.

Perhaps it was my imagination, but I thought there was an underlying note of concern in her voice.

"Thank you," I replied. "I might just do that."

Then with the grace of a ballerina she walked away. With my eyes I followed her progress until she disappeared around the bend at the foot of Bray Head. It was easy to keep track of her in her vibrant yellow tee-shirt and bright orange shorts. She looked like summer. I felt dowdy, and worn out.

When enough time had passed for the room to be serviced I returned there, and lying down on the bed fell asleep. After a few hours I awoke feeling groggy and totally miserable.

"This is no way to live," I muttered, as I contrasted my existence with the lives of the people I could see from my window enjoying all that the beach had to offer. Then I did what I hadn't done for a number of weeks; sitting down at the dressing table mirror I looked at my face. The eyes that stared back at me were dark rimmed and tired looking. My skin was dry, lined, and dull. Vertical lines were puckered around my mouth. My forehead had train tracks on it. I looked like an old woman. Tara Arnould came to mind. We were the same age, but she looked at least ten years younger than I. Yet, not that terribly long before, she had looked twenty years older. She had, by whatever means, pulled herself back from the brink and was offering me the chance to do the same. I had often heard my less scientific colleagues say; "When the pupil is ready the teacher appears." I had never been one for that kind of airy-fairy stuff, but what had I to lose?

I found the community centre without any difficulty. The little map on the back of Tara's business card was easy to follow. Although only a five minute walk from the Main Street, I had never been on Killarney Road before, since it was on the opposite side of the town to the beach around which all our childhood activities had revolved.

Bray's Community Centre was not at all as I had expected. In my experience they were usually rectangular shaped, grey, boxlike, cement structures, with high windows, presumably to reduce the risk of vandalism. When you had seen one you'd seen them all. But in Bray the community centre was an imposing, two storied, red-bricked house, standing well back from the road. The car park to the front was nearly full. I began to feel anxious. What if there were crowds of people there? What if there was someone who knew me? What if I got a panic attack? What if Tara mentioned that I was a doctor; would I be expected to have all the answers? I stood for a moment unsure of what to do next. Then, as if in slow motion, I saw myself as I had been just a few days earlier; having to flee the supermarket in panic. "I've nothing to lose," I thought and walked quickly to the door before I changed my mind.

Inside the building was a hive of activity. Music, laughter, and chat drifted out as the doors to classes were opened to admit boys and girls, some in Irish dancing costumes, some in karate suits, and men and women with books and copies in hand, to various rooms.

In reception I asked if I could sign up for Tara's class.

"The Good Vibrations Course?" the receptionist asked, looking at me for confirmation.

I had no idea what the course was called, or indeed what it was about.

"Tara Arnould's course," I repeated. She nodded.

"There's no need to sign up for the Good Vibrations Course. Just go along to room two, down the hall, it's the second door on the left."

"Do I pay you or Tara?" I asked as an afterthought.

"Oh Tara makes her own arrangements about payment," she said using her hands in a dismissive manner. "She's a great believer in the barter system. Don't worry about money. That will all work out."

The door to room two was open. I went in and sat on the chair nearest the exit to facilitate a quick getaway if necessary. With a furtive glance I calculated that there were about five other people there. But no one spoke. There was a distinct feeling of unease, an uncomfortable silence which was broken, only occasionally, by the sound of a whispered comment.

At 8 o'clock Tara came in. When she entered it was as if the whole dynamic in the room changed. She was literally like a breath of fresh air. Her dress was a simple, white, knee-length cotton sheath covered in vibrant splashes of colour. It flattered her curves and accentuated her waist. It was pure simplicity. She wore her shining chestnut hair in a loose bouffant style. Her makeup was minimal, just a little coral lipstick and smoky green eye-shadow which accentuated her sparkling hazel eyes. Dangling golden earrings, worn with a matching necklace and bracelet, completed her outfit. When she passed there was a lingering smell of roses. She was absolutely beautiful. By comparison with her, the rest of us looked positively ill.

While I was certain that her arrival into the room had had an uplifting effect on me I could only imagine that we were having the opposite effect on her. However her demeanour gave no indication of

17

this as she continued to smile brightly while inviting us to place our chairs in a circle.

Seated in the circle it was easy to see the other people who were present. Directly across from me was a man of indeterminable age, not because it wasn't obvious from his face, but because his face wasn't visible. In fact his whole body was hidden behind a confusion of unkempt, matted, faded red hair, beard, and crumpled clothing. The slobbers of that day's, or some other day's dinner decorated the front of his jumper. An old shopping bag lay on the floor beside his dirty sneakers. It seemed to be full of newspapers.

"David," he said when it came to his turn to introduce himself. That was all, a mumbled, practically inaudible, "David", no smile, no gentle inflection, just "David." Had I been compelled to supply one word to describe him it would have been "disastrous." Then a thought came to me. I decided that I would monitor the effectiveness of the course by the improvement in his outer appearance. He would be my yardstick. If the course impacted positively on him then I would have to judge it as being exceptionally successful.

I sensed that the elderly lady seated beside him was sad. She was tiny. Her little slacks and top could have been purchased in the children's department of any store. While they were clean, they were a mismatch in style and colour; as if she was using them for the sole purpose of covering her petite body. Her thick, snow-white hair had the potential to be beautiful. Had it been expertly cut it could have complimented her heart shaped face and large blue eyes. However it just hung down in "I couldn't be bothered" mode, increasing her drawn, worn out look. This added to the air of fragility and depression which exuded from her. But when she smiled, as she did when introducing herself as, "Rose," her eyes lit up momentarily. I could well-imagine her as a fun-loving person, before something had broken her heart.

While Liz and I were in no way alike physically, I felt that we were experiencing the same condition. I recognized the overly anxious look in her eyes, like that of an animal caught in traffic. It was the look which

I knew gave expression to the terror I felt when my whole system churned in panic. She too was very ill at ease, constantly looking from her watch to the clock on the wall, as if willing the hands on both to move more quickly, perhaps fearing, as I did, the arrival of the next panic attack.

The hand holding man and woman to her left were very obviously a couple. Physically they were by far the healthiest looking members of the group; tanned, and slim. I reckoned they were in their mid-forties. Mike was about one metre eighty centimetres tall, (six feet two inches) with a round, pleasant face and smiling eyes which his receding hairline only served to accentuate. By comparison Carol was tiny, about one metre fifty, but despite that they bore a striking resemblance to one another having the same shaped face and eyes. They could easily have passed for brother and sister.

While petite, Carol was in no way fragile looking. She struck me as a real outdoor girl. Her tawny blonde hair was cut just below her ears. A hint of lip gloss was all the makeup she wore. There was no need for anything else; her light tan gave her a healthy glow. While both were expensively dressed their clothes were well worn, and apart from her wedding ring, Carol sported no jewellery. There was an air of faded prosperity about them. I reckoned Mike and Carol had seen better days.

"Welcome everybody," Tara began as the door opened slowly and a tall emaciated man entered. She immediately vacated her chair and motioned for him to sit there. While the circle moved to accommodate another person I observed the latest member to join the group. Sean's physical attributes would have cut a dash in any company. He was of above average height and was blessed with a mop of dark brown hair, the same colour as his eyes. But rather than walking tall and confi-dently, as a young man like him would be expected to, his head was bowed and his shoulders stooped, as if he was trying to pass unnoticed. He sat on the chair which Tara had vacated for him without acknowl-edging, or engaging, with anyone. A distinct air of discontent exuded from him as he sat slumped, with his head down. This resulted in him looking out at the world from under his eyebrows, a look which I found disturbing, to say the least.

We were indeed a motley crew. Looking around it was obvious that everyone there was in need of the good vibrations which the course promised. That was the common denominator which had brought us together. That and Tara. When she started to speak I immediately returned my attention to her.

"Before we begin there are a few ground rules which I wish to set down," she said. "Firstly, anything that is said in the group is treated with the strictest confidence. Of course that doesn't apply to anything I say. That is absolutely for public consumption. If you think something could be of assistance to anybody else please, please, share it with them.

Secondly, no one will be asked to identify themselves other than by their first name, or to disclose their reason for being here, or indeed anything about themselves, unless they wish to. This is a stress free zone for you. I'm the one who has to come up with the goods," she laughed.

"Thirdly, if you have any questions, please ask. Don't be afraid that you will be thought foolish. You can be sure that if something is unclear to you, someone else in the group is having the same difficulty. They'll thank you for asking, and so will I. I'm not for a minute suggesting that I have all the answers, but between us we have a lot of experience. We will all benefit from sharing our knowledge.

Fourthly, please continue with your medication until your doctor instructs you otherwise. Modern medicine is amazing. Whatever you learn during this course is intended to complement conventional medicine, not to replace it.

Finally I would like you to end each session by going to The Tea Cup for a cup of tea or coffee, and a wind down. Are these rules clear and acceptable to everyone?" she asked as she placed a bundle of folders on the table behind her.

We nodded. That is how the course began; the course which proved to be the most enlightening experience of my life.

ENERGY

"No matter why you are here, no matter what problem you are facing, I would like to assure you that it can be addressed by using the strategies which I will suggest; strategies which allow us to access the positive vibrations of health, beauty, and happiness which are all around us," Tara said by way of introduction to her good vibrations course.

"This is not a silly illusion," she assured us as I sat up and took notice.

"The greatest minds in the universe have proven that everything in the world, including us, is composed of vibrations which establish a particular frequency, and that everything on the same frequency influences everything else on that wavelength. So it follows that if we wish to access love, health, happiness, or indeed any other positive attribute all we need to do is to tune into the correct frequency. This is the basis of quantum physics. It's the principle which allows radio, telephone, internet and all manner of electronic communication."

While I had no idea what the course was about, I hadn't expected it to be based on any of Einstein's theories.

"When we know how to tap into this positive energy, we are better able to cope, more optimistic, more capable of thinking outside the box, more inclined to look for alternatives, more proactive," she continued with great conviction.

I thought it sounded too good to be true.

"That positive vibrations support all aspects of human life is proven by the personal experiences of some of the greatest minds, and the scientific evidence of the latest developments," she said, indicating the pile of folders on the table, making it obvious that we could access that information there.

"As the name suggests everything good and beautiful is on the positive vibrations wavelength," she continued. "All we need to know is how to tap into it, how to get onto that frequency and tune into that energy. Then we will be vigorous, dynamic, and powerful."

While I desperately wanted to believe what she was saying I found it difficult to accept that we could possibly do as she was suggesting. It sounded ludicrous; ludicrous but awesome.

"This is not a silly unattainable objective," she continued as if picking up on my disbelief. "Its veracity can be easily demonstrated. Imagine something beautiful, something that makes you feel happy."

I couldn't do it.

"Think of someone you love," she repeated as if aware of the problem I was having. My two year old nephew, Colm, came to mind. I imagined him waddling along in his own inimitable fashion, refusing all help, as he tried to make his way independently on very unsteady feet. I could physically feel my mood lift as a result of the surge of love which I felt for him.

"You have felt good for a brief moment because you have tuned into the frequency of something positive," Tara said. "When we learn how to tap into this energy permanently we experience a totally new form of existence. We are like radio receivers picking up the positive energy of the forces of the universe. We are powered by the same source as the sun, wind, and tides; unlimited energy is available to us. All we need to do is to tune into the correct frequency. Then we will access the highest possible vibrations and pulsate with the energy of everything that is good and beautiful and healthy. This will have huge positive consequences for us. We will be more alive, more dynamic, and more vivacious because energy is life, and life is energy. Without energy we are lifeless. We may be alive, but we are not living."

That was exactly my situation. I was alive but not living. Since Lucy's death I hadn't the energy to do any of the things which gave me pleasure. I didn't meet my friends. I didn't go walking, or dancing, or swimming, or to my art or language classes. I just went home from work and collapsed onto a chair, trying to conserve the little energy I had. Yet I was still drained. Despite my scepticism of what Tara had said there was no doubt but that she was correct about life being a non-event without energy. She had been right about something else too. When imagining Colm I had, for an instant, felt better.

"Very soon we'll learn how to tap into this limitless life force which is all around us," she continued with authority, as if it was the most natural thing in the world to do.

"But firstly I'd like to say a little about the internal receptors which tune us into the vibrations of power," she continued. "They are called chakras, or energy centres. The word means wheel because when working efficiently, and when taking in universal energy, they spin like a wheel. It is the vibration of this spinning wheel which powers us. Sometimes, for various reasons, our chakras are damaged causing them to close down either fully or partially. When this happens our energy supply is cut off, or restricted, and we become ill, depressed, anxious, and unable to cope. During this course we will learn how to keep the chakras open and how to power them to ensure that they work to their optimum to provide us with the energy we need for everyday life."

Then she passed around some sheets of paper which she had taken from the table behind her. They showed the outline of a body cocooned in what appeared to be a rainbow of colour. Little circles, numbered from one to seven, stretched the length of the spine from its base to the crown of the head.

"This is how exponents of energy medicine view the body," she explained indicating the orb of light. "They can see, or feel, the body's energy field, sometimes referred to as the aura. It has been described by seers as a Technicolor halo of light which surrounds each one of us, and is a product of the light emanating from the energy centres which are situated at various locations all along the body. The vibrancy of the aura is indicative of the health of the chakras; the brighter the aura, the healthier the energy system. Proponents of energy medicine believe that this system is the blueprint of the body. This is where they differ from modern medicine. In conventional medicine the body is divided up into a series of systems; the nervous system, the digestive system, the circulatory system, the lymphatic system, all separate, all requiring different specialists and types of treatment. In energy medicine all illness, physical, mental, or emotional is believed to stem from one source; a malfunction in the chakra system. Once that malfunction has been addressed, the illness will disappear."

Tara's next utterance struck a chord with me. She said that since the energy body is seen as the entity's blueprint it is believed that illness is first manifest there. That it is actually far advanced before it becomes visible in the physical. This, she suggested, explained the phenomena of medical tests coming back clear, only for the person to be diagnosed, a very short time later, with a well progressed serious illness. That was exactly what had happened with Lucy. Her tests had all been clear, yet that killer had been lurking in her brain. Could energy medicine have saved her? There was no way of knowing, but I was impressed with Tara's observation. It sounded feasible.

"Now I would like to give you a brief introduction to the energy system before getting down to the more important task of advising on how to address any problems," she said.

"There are seven major chakras, or energy centres. The base chakra is located here," she continued, indicating the circle at the bottom of the spine marked with the number one.

"The second is in the area of the reproductive organs, the solar plexus houses the third, the chest and the throat are the locations of the fourth and fifth chakras, the sixth is in the centre of the forehead above the bridge of the nose, and the seventh is on the crown of the head," she said, indicating each one in turn.

"As is obvious from their locations they influence not only the most important organs and muscle groups, but also the hormone producing glands. We are all aware of the power of hormones," she continued. "I'm sure we all know someone who has to inject insulin because of diabetes, or ingest thyroid hormones because of a malfunction in that gland, or is on some other form of hormone replacement therapy. But we may not fully appreciate the power of these tiny secretions. We may not realise that they impact, not only on the physical, but on every aspect of our lives. They influence the way we feel, our reproductive system, how we digest our food, our moods, our physical and mental development, our ability and our achievements. To maintain good

health it is vital that we are aware of the location of the glands producing these secretions. Then we will know which chakra we need to concentrate on to ensure the production of the necessary hormones."

That was quite a statement I felt. It sounded to me as if she was
suggesting that if the chakras were working properly that the body
would automatically maintain the correct level of hormones. And that
even if a chakra had stopped working, that it could be activated again.
In effect she was saying that the body could repair itself. The idea of
that was awesome, but then wasn't that exactly what she had done?
Since the last time I had seen her she had completely rejuvenated physically, mentally and emotionally. I determined that I wasn't going to
miss a word as she gave a quick summary of the function of each
chakra.

Starting with the one at the base of the spine she indicated that it
was responsible for the production of the sex hormones; oestrogen,
and testosterone. She mentioned the importance of these hormones
to our health; physical, mental, and social, saying that a lack may result
in depression, in a loss of confidence, in feelings of inadequacy and an
inability to cope. Our attractiveness to others was, she said, determined by the confidence, energy, and self-assurance which attests to
the proper level of these hormones in the system. She also said that
this is where adrenaline, the get up and go hormone, is produced.

She referred to the second chakra as the area of our pleasure centre
governing our creativity, sexual desires, and our appetites for food and
alcohol.

"When working properly we feel content, loyal and satisfied," she
said. "Addictions on the other hand signal that this chakra needs help
and attention," here she paused for a second, as if for emphasis.

While I couldn't explain why, I immediately got the feeling that she
was stressing this point for the benefit of someone in the group. Was
she aware that someone there had a problem with addiction? Was she
trying to communicate to them that this course could help? Did she
wish to indicate that their problem was due to a malfunction in the area
of the second chakra and could be addressed by activating that chakra?

That was the impression I got from her, and I hoped that whoever was suffering in that way would get hope from her words. She also pointed out that, as was obvious from its location, the second chakra played a very important part in the digestive system because of its influence on the intestines, the liver, spleen and pancreas.

She identified an area above the navel and below the chest as the solar plexus or third chakra. This chakra also played a very important part in the digestive process through its influence on the stomach, pancreas and spleen, she informed us.

"I'm sure everyone here is aware of the consequences of a malfunctioning pancreas," she said. "Diabetes is extremely common. Some people can control it by diet, and others must inject insulin to keep the amount of sugar in the blood at a safe level. If untreated this condition can have devastating consequences; affecting not only the body, but also the mind and emotions. Out of balance the patient may feel depressed, lack energy, feel isolated, hopeless, even suicidal," she said.

I thought of Helen Murray, one of my patients; poor sad, depressed, Helen. But I didn't let my mind wander. I wanted to keep focussed.

"By contrast when the correct balance exists one is in touch with the centre of our inner knowing; the gut feeling, which informs our decision making and leads to increased optimism and confidence," she continued.

"There is no prize for guessing the function of the heart chakra" she said indicating the circle containing the number four. "It is to keep the heart healthy. And when the heart is healthy we feel contented, joyful and fun loving."

I looked around the circle at the group of sad looking people. It didn't take a degree in medicine to know that all those hearts were in need of help. Personally I felt that I would never again manifest the positive emotions of a healthy heart. I couldn't imagine ever feeling happy again. But I certainly didn't want to feel the bitterness, envy, resentment, or hatred, which Tara said indicated energy problems in this area. According to her this power centre was responsible, not alone for the health of the heart, but for the health of the whole body since it powers the thymus gland which forms a crucial part of the immune system. By transferring white blood cells into T cells, which are then transported to various other lymph glands, it plays an important part in fighting infection and disease.

"The area of the throat is extremely important, because there are a number of hormone producing glands here," she said pointing to the fifth circle. "A malfunctioning thyroid gland results in an imbalance in its life enhancing hormone; an oversupply of which leads to hyperactivity, nervousness, and emotional unbalance, an inadequate supply causes the bodily movements to slow down, leading to weight gain and a drop in body temperature. This is also the location of the parathyroid," she continued. "Its function is to regulate the amount of calcium in the blood. An inadequate supply of this element impedes proper nerve functioning and can lead to nervousness, muscle twitching, convulsions and even death. The health of the mouth, salivary glands, neck, and teeth are also dependent on the throat chakra," she said looking around at the group, all of whom were listening intently. "When functioning properly we can express our thoughts in appropriate language, we can vocalise without fear. We speak up for ourselves in an appropriate manner. When it is out of balance our creativity is blocked and replaced by feelings of rejection and paranoia. Serenity and poise are a result of the proper functioning of the parathyroid," she said and smiled.

Her glands were obviously working effectively, I thought. There was an air of calm about her, and she very definitely had the ability to communicate well, having spoken with clarity and authority for the past hour without referring to any notes or aids.

"There are many cultures which consider the sixth chakra to be the location of an invisible eye which provides perception beyond ordinary sight," she said pointing to an area in the centre of the forehead.

"Many traditional Chinese religious sects practice third eye training. The goal of this training is to allow students to tune into the correct vibrations of the universe and to reach more advanced levels of meditation. They believe that the third eye leads to inner realms and places of higher consciousness. This chakra is very important to the health of the body since it influences the hypothalamus and pituitary glands. These glands ensure that the correct nerve impulses and hormones are circulated in the blood to maintain balance and health in the whole system. When this chakra is malfunctioning we became mean and absent minded. When it is working properly we are aware, wise and knowledgeable.

And this is the centre of our consciousness and spirituality," she said pointing to the circle containing the number seven, located on the crown of the head.

"It is the chakra through which universal energy enters the body, and so it is essential that it is kept open. Since it is the centre of our spirituality it resonates with the God vibration; the vibration of creativity. So it is charged by spending time outdoors in nature, at the beach, in the countryside, anywhere where creation is awesome. We can also charge it by tuning into our own imagination and creating something beautiful and positive ourselves. Another very effective and immediate way to open and energise this power centre is to make direct communication with whoever you believe the Creator to be. The Lord's Prayer is recommended as a very effective way of charging this chakra."

When she had finished speaking she sat quietly for a moment. This gave me an opportunity to recap on all the symptoms of a malfunctioning energy system which were relevant to me. I had no vitality. I was tired, anxious, and unable to sleep. I had no appetite, and was indecisive, forgetful, and felt very, very low. When I took a quick glance around I caught Liz's eye. Her expression left me in no doubt but that she too had compiled an inventory of ills. Her raised eyebrows and head shake suggested that, like me, she felt that she was also a hopeless case.

In stark contrast to our reaction, when Tara spoke it was apparent that she felt in no way daunted by what I conceived as the insurmountable task of restoring us to good health. She seemed to take it as a given that revitalising our energy systems was possible, and would result in us pulsating with power, feeling vital and alive, capable of grabbing life with both hands. We would be dynamic and able to take on the world, lighting up our own lives and energising all around us. That was how she described a properly charged body. It sounded amazing. I had forgotten that it was possible to feel that way. Then she told us what we all wanted, indeed needed to hear. She told us how we were going to make that happen.

"The way to power the chakras is to expose them to every possible positive vibration available to us. And of course the most positive healing vibration of all is love. This is the bedrock of all major philosophies and healing therapies," she said as I remembered how the feeling of love which I had experienced while thinking of Colm had, for an instant, relieved my heartache.

"As you will see in the course notes, giving and receiving love has been proven by scientific research to both open and charge the chakras. And that love must start with the self. We must first love ourselves if we wish others to love us. If by the manner in which we live, or present ourselves, we make it obvious that we feel unworthy of love, then we are cutting off a huge life-enhancing resource; the love of others for us."

David shifted his clearly uncared for body on the chair. As far as I was concerned he was a testimony to what she was saying. "How could anyone love him?" I thought. "He doesn't love himself enough even to wash."

"We must manifest this love for self by treating ourselves as we would the person we love most in the world. And by making our environment as beautiful for ourselves as we would if a very important dignitary was coming to visit us."

David once again looked extremely uncomfortable.

"Loving yourself does not necessarily involve any monetary outlay," she continued. "In fact some of the most powerful and positive vibrations cost absolutely nothing. They are found in the words we speak. Using positive affirmations is essential to us all, and most particularly to those of us who have been abused, ridiculed, or put down as children. Affirming ourselves now, as adults, helps to redress that damage, and to assert that we are worthy of the love we were denied."

It was obvious from David's body language that Tara's words were having an impact on him. Initially he fiddled, pulled at his beard, and shifted his position many times, as if trying to rid himself of agitation, but as she continued to speak he progressively leaned forward and concentrated on her every word.

"One of the most powerful and easiest ways of loving the self is to affirm yourself every day. It is an extremely potent strategy," she said, as approaching David, she asked him to stand up and to repeat aloud; "I'm weak, I'm weak, I'm weak."

He repeated the phrase about twenty times. Then, requesting that he stretch out his strongest arm, she placed one hand on his shoulder and the other on his wrist telling him to resist her force. When she pressed on his arm it dropped like a stone. That was surprising, because despite his dishevelled appearance, David was physically much bigger than Tara. He looked as if he could lift her up in one hand. She then asked him to repeat; "I'm strong, I'm strong, I'm strong," a number of times. On this occasion, when she conducted the experiment again, his arm stayed strong. I was amazed, but not as amazed as David was, if facial expressions were anything to go by.

"Keep the thoughts positive," she advised. "For most of us, that involves changing the record in our heads and programming ourselves in a self-affirming way. But the dividends are worth the effort. Make your thoughts your allies. They are very powerful, and they're free."

"Another positive strategy is to act as if," she continued, indicating with her hands that she wished us all to stand up. We obeyed rather cautiously.

"So much for a stress free zone," I thought.

"Pretend that you are actors," she said. "Imagine you are playing the part of a beautiful, young, healthy, fit, happy person."

In my state that was too much to ask. Looking around the room it was clear that I wasn't the only one having that problem. I noticed Sean in particular. He stood like a gangling teenager with his head bowed and his arms hanging awkwardly by his sides.

"Please try to dispel the lethargy," Tara said shaking her hands and legs vigorously. "I know it can be difficult."

"Do you really?" Sean asked in an audible whisper.

"Think of someone who is powerful, strong and vigorous," Tara continued calmly.

Dr. Steven's wife, Caroline, came to mind. She was dynamic, confident and beautiful.

"Imagine how that person feels. Stand as they stand."

Immediately my posture changed dramatically. I stood up straighter; my shoulders dropped and fell back causing my chest to expand. I held my head up. Glancing around the room it seemed that some people had taken her instructions on board more than others. David and Sean both still stood with their heads down, shoulders rounded.

"How do you feel?" she asked.

"Better," I replied truthfully, more than surprised by the difference such a small adjustment had made.

"Now pretend that you are depressed, sad, lonely, old and infirm," she suggested. This resulted in us all assuming a stance which seemed to mimic that of David and Sean, with stooped backs, bowed heads, and pained grim faces.

"How do you feel now?"

"Very down and unhappy," I replied.

This time, when she asked us to revert to the stance of youth, I noticed that David had made an effort to straighten up. Now everyone in the group, with the exception of Sean whose posture hadn't changed, looked bigger, more robust and confident. Just a thought had taken years off us. There was no denying the power of the strategy which she had just suggested. The proof was there, before my very eyes.

"That's very scary and wonderful isn't it?" she asked. "By just imitating the stance and expressions which signify a particular characteristic we can access the vibration of that quality. By assuming the posture, by using the facial and hand gestures, by speaking in a tone that signifies a particular trait, we can tap into its vibration and access its power. So from now on I would like you to remember this exercise and to always act as if you are strong, confident, and in control. A good way to incorporate both these strategies of self-affirmation is, when under pressure, to do as we have done, to affirm that you are happy, strong, and capable. Repeat the words savouring every one of them, absorbing their vibration, and then, when you feel ready, assume the posture you believe portrays that state. In so doing you will tune into that strong, capable, happy, vibration and your body and mind will improve beyond your imaginings. Trust me and please try," she said with a sincerity which communicated a sense of caring.

When we were seated again she asked Sean to sit up with his back straight, and to place both feet flat on the floor. I thought that she was very brave to approach him, given his attitude. But on reflection it was probably her way of letting him know that she bore him no resentment.

Her direction required a huge change in his posture. Up to that point he had been slumped in the chair with his arms and legs crossed defensively. It was only then I noticed that everyone in the group, including myself, was sitting with their knees crossed.

Then, repeating the experiment which she had performed earlier, she asked him to extend his strongest arm outwards at shoulder level, advising him to resist the pressure she was applying to it. His arm stayed strong.

"Cross your legs," she instructed and then placed one of her hands on his shoulder and the other on the back of his wrist. His arm dropped like a dead weight. We all shifted our positions.

"As we've just heard universal energy flows into us through the crown chakra at the top of the head. Our structure must be balanced properly for our systems to receive that energy and to process it correctly. It is our responsibility to facilitate the uninterrupted flow of that energy if we wish to stay healthy. The spine should be straight at all times, with both feet flat on the floor. Sitting with the legs crossed or, worse still, sitting on the legs, knocks the skeletal frame out of position. The knees, hips, and shoulder joints, together with the spine, are forced out of alignment. This in turn seriously impedes energy flow, resulting in pain and illness. The physiology reflects the psychology," she said stressing that for good health it is essential to keep the body well balanced. She finished by adding that a good rule of thumb was to keep the shoulders and hips in line.

To say that I was more than surprised by the content of the course is an understatement. Within the space of an hour Tara had demonstrated the power of three simple strategies, previously unknown to me, which anyone could use, anywhere and at any time to increase their energy levels. It was clear that she had knowledge which I didn't have, and I was sure that the converse was also true. We were the products of different experiences and disciplines. But I was there to find out what she knew and not to display what I knew by questioning her and trying to refute what she said. So I decided that the best way for me to get the most benefit from the course was to listen to her, to try whatever she suggested, no matter how unscientific it appeared, and if it did me good to incorporate it into my life.

Had the class ended there I would have considered the evening very well spent, and indeed I was just about to reach for my bag when she advised us to sit up straight with the feet flat on the floor.

"Love is the healing vibration and smiling energy is healing energy," she said as she placed her right palm on top of her left and rested her hands on her lap. We did likewise. Then she talked us through a body journey which involved bathing each organ, gland, and important muscle in the energy of a healing, loving, smile. Once again she asked us to close the eyes and to picture the face of someone, or something we loved. She then instructed us to smile brightly at the source of our inspiration, to connect with the loving emotion which we felt for it, and to bring that loving feeling back to the eyes bathing them in the intensity of the positive emotion of love. Smiling lovingly at them we thanked them sincerely for the wonderful work which they perform for us, and for all the pleasure which they give us. Then she instructed us to ask them to please continue to work well. As we felt the tension around the eyes relax in response to the inner smile, Tara suggested that we bring the energy of the smile to the area of the mid brow, and from there to let it wash over the face, down the nose, cheeks, into the mouth over the tongue, teeth, and gums, all the while thanking each part for the function it performed.

"Imagine the healing energy of the smile washing down the throat and coaxing open the thyroid gland," she suggested.

In response to the emotion of love which we were lavishing on it we were to visualise it opening like a flower and secreting extra energy into the body. We then thanked it and asked it to please continue its very vital job of powering us. This was the format we followed as we bathed the thymus, heart, lungs, liver, kidneys, adrenals, pancreas, spleen and genital area in the light of the healing smile. Then reconnecting with the love object we smiled all along the length of the digestive system from the mouth to the stomach and intestines. We visualised each section as young and healthy and thanked it for contributing positively to our health. Finally, after once again charging our smile with the positive energy of love, we illuminated the inside of the skull with the healing smile. Tara said this would result in the pineal, pituitary and hypothalamus glands producing the hormones necessary to keep the body in perfect health. Then we smiled all the way down the spine and thanked each vertebra for working tirelessly to enable us to move painlessly and with ease.

When we had completed the body journey we were given the time to sit, relax, and to scan the body to identify any area of residual discomfort. The ache in my heart, which was ever present since Lucy's death, was still there. I tried to smile it away, but without success.

Finally, in order to seal the positive energy at our centres, Tara instructed us to trace a circle outwards from the navel for a count of thirty six; women in a counter-clockwise direction, men in a clockwise direction. To finish the women were to spiral inwards in a clockwise direction for a count of twenty four, men in a counter-clockwise direction.

"On the subject of self-love may I make one more observation before we go?" Tara asked checking the time on her watch.

"It will only take five minutes," she added.

When nobody objected she continued. "Another powerful loving strategy is to keep our essence intact by validating ourselves, by giving ourselves permission to be our own inimitable selves, by using the talents which we have been given which mark us out as unique, and by developing our own distinctive style, rather than trying to be a copy of someone else. I must aspire to be the best me that I can be, not the best copy of you, or anyone else that I can be. In order to show love to ourselves we have a responsibility to express our own individuality by surrounding ourselves with possessions which reflect our own individual taste, not that of someone else.

And if we truly love our bodies we will consider them worthy of the best care we can provide. That must include clothing them in clothes that are uniquely ours, not the clothes of someone else, someone whose state of health, or whose values, are unknown to us; someone whose vibrations could disturb ours. It is imperative that the vibrations we bring to our bodies are pure, good, healthy and healing. Since we cannot know with certainty what vibrations clothes carry, we are better to buy our own."

I thought for a moment that David was going to be ill. His face had turned an ashen colour and he looked very uncomfortable as Tara illustrated the point she had just made by reading from a very old book; "For the health of the entity, the only cast offs tolerable are those of one's guru. These alone can be certain of carrying such good vibrations as to support wellbeing."

She then quoted the law of entrainment in physics to further illustrate her point. I remembered that law from science class. It states that two objects in close proximity affect one another. Similarly, she suggested, that we are influenced by the people and things around us; that they can sap our energy and cause disease.

While Liz passed around the folders Tara opened one and held up some stapled sheets.

"These studies scientifically prove the power of love," she said. "I hope you will find that they make interesting reading."

Then holding up a single green sheet she continued; "I urge you to read and reread this, to internalise it, and to apply it in your lives immediately. Start by being gentle and kind with yourself. Manifest this kindness every day by treating yourself to something that you love, just for the sheer pleasure of it."

Then identifying a single yellow sheet as a speech by Nelson Mandela, she advised us to read it over and over until we could recall it at will anytime we felt unsure, or sad, or alone.

Then wishing us a very good night she left the room.

When we repaired to The Tea Cup, John, the owner, showed us to a circular table set for seven in a cosy alcove. When he had removed the paper serviettes which were covering the plates of fresh sandwiches, he went into the kitchen and returned with a large pot of tea. One of the waitresses then brought a pot of coffee. We all sat down in silence. David nodded as he placed his chair beside mine. I was aware of a slight smell of alcohol mixed with body odour.

"How could anyone love him?" I found myself thinking again, feeling quite nauseous as I tried to counteract the unpleasant smell by sniffing the perfume on my wrist. Afraid that the discomfort I was feeling might lead to a panic attack, I drank my tea hurriedly and left just as John was placing plates of warm scones on the table.

There was a great buzz in the Promenade Bar when I returned to the hotel. A notice on the reception desk advised that the monthly meeting of the Bray Singers' Group was the crowd puller. Under normal circumstances I would have enjoyed the sing-song very much, but not now. Now I was exhausted. I went immediately to my room and lay down on the bed. The smiling face which Tara had exhibited that night, side by side with the agonised face she had presented with in the surgery, came to mind. That spurred me into action. I determined once again that no matter how off the wall they seemed, I was going to follow her recommendations to the letter. Standing up, in the nearest thing to power mode that I could manage, I walked around with my spine straight and my head held high. When I had completed a few circuits of the room, affirming that I was strong and capable, I sat down at the dressing table and opened the course folder. I was too tired to study the stapled sheets, but Nelson Mandela's speech made compelling reading:

"Our deepest fear is not that we are inadequate,

Our deepest fear is that we are powerful beyond measure, it is our light, not our darkness, that most frightens us. We ask ourselves who am I to be brilliant, gorgeous, talented and fabulous?

Actually, who are you not to be? You are a child of God. Your playing small doesn't serve the world. There is nothing enlightened about shrinking so that other people won't feel insecure around you. We are born to make manifest the glory of God that is within us. It's not just in some of us; it's in everyone. And as we let our own light shine, we unconsciously give other people permission to do the same. As we are liberated from our own fear, our presence automatically liberates others."

It was so beautiful that I read it a few more times before taking up the second sheet. This reading I recognised as St. Paul's letter to the Corinthians. Only three months previously I had read it at a friend's wedding. But it hadn't registered then. Now I articulated every word and deliberated on its meaning. I intended to incorporate its wisdom into my life:

Love is gentle.

Love is kind.

Love is not jealous or boastful:

It is not arrogant or rude.

Love does not insist on its own way.

It is not resentful.

It does not rejoice in wrong, but rejoices in the truth.

Love believes all things.

Love bears all things.

Hopes all things.

Endures all things.

Charity never falls away, whether prophesies shall be made void or tongues shall cease, or knowledge be destroyed.

And now these three remain faith, hope and charity, and the greatest of these is charity."

At the bottom of the sheet Tara had added the most important points from that night's session.

Love is the healing vibration.

Smiling energy is healing energy.

Love yourself

Affirm yourself

Act as if

Carry yourself with love.

In the stillness of the night I awoke in terror trying to escape the demon-like creatures that mocked and poked me. My distress was further compounded by the fact that I was completely disoriented. The bedside lamp, whose light usually helped comfort me in these types of situations, was not there when I tried to turn it on. This added further to my panic. Where was I? What was happening to me? Had I lost my reason? After some time I remembered that I was not at home. Reaching out I felt for the switch on the wall beside the bed. When I pressed it blessed light dispelled the frightening darkness. The notes of the previous night's class lay crumpled on the bed beside me.

Love is the healing vibration.
Smiling energy is healing energy.
Love yourself.
Affirm yourself.
Act as if.
Carry yourself with love.

When I awoke again, having drifted off into a fitful sleep, the sun was streaming in through the east facing window. It was 6 a.m. Normally I'd have been preparing to go to work. Now I got up and looked out at the sea. Already there were people on the promenade. Those hurrying along in business suits were obviously on their way to the train station which was situated at the northern, harbour end, of the beach. From there The Dublin Area Rapid Transit line, [DART] brought commuters to the city centre in the space of forty five minutes. On route they enjoyed stunning views of Dublin Bay, which many have described as being as spectacular as the Bay of Naples. Joggers pounded along, while dog walkers strolled, or stood awkwardly still, depending on their animal's mood and level of interest in the flag poles which lined the way. I was reminded of the fun we had as children playing with Eddie. But I dismissed that thought immediately. I couldn't bear to think about it. Instead I moved to sit on the stool in front of the dressing table. My reflection in the mirror steeled my resolve of the previous night, my resolve to emulate Tara Arnould. And the first thing I was going to do was to eat. I knew my body needed the nourishment, but the thought of facing into the dining room on my own was a little unnerving. I was afraid I'd panic and have to make a quick exit. Once again Tara's advice came to mind. "Be positive," she had said. "Change the record."

"I'm calm, I'm calm, I'm calm," I repeated to myself all the way downstairs. Then, as a contingency plan, I decided that if all came to all I would go to sit on the little armchair in the nook off the foyer. I would be safe there.

However there was no need to worry. I helped myself from the buffet table and ate a pleasant meal. Nobody paid any attention. Everyone was so occupied with their own company that they didn't even notice me.

After breakfast I took a copy of the daily paper from the reception desk and spent the morning reading it in the sunny conservatory to the front of the hotel. When my eyes got tired I passed the time watching the people on the promenade. I obviously dozed off because I was wakened by the noise of the guests going in to lunch. Once again I steeled myself and got through the meal without incident. Then I returned to my room, watched a movie on television and snoozed a little. The rest of the day was spent drifting in and out of sleep with the words of St. Paul in my hand.

When I felt a little more rested I opened the course folder and read:

In energy medicine love is seen as the highest vibration. This belief is endorsed by some of humanities greatest and noblest minds.

"Where there is love there is life," Mahatma Gandhi, Indian Spiritual Leader.

"To me life has meaning because of love." Eleanor Roosevelt, American Humanitarian

"Love is the ultimate and the highest goal to which we can aspire......salvation is through love and in love." Victor Frankl, Austrian Psychiatrist.

Scientific evidence of the importance of love for good health:

In 2012 research led by Dr. Joan Luby, child psychiatrist and neuroscientist at the Washington University School of Medicine St. Louis found that school age children raised in a nurturing environment typically do better in school and are more emotionally developed than non nurtured peers.

Research conducted by Glen Jenson, Utah State University Family and Human Development professor, found that people who feel loved, or when it's reciprocated, live longer, happier lives, and have better health and make more money.

Yale scientists surveyed 119 men and 40 women before they submitted to angiography tests. Those who reported feeling loved and supported were found to have less blockages in the arteries according to the Smart Marriage web site; The Coalition for Marriage, Family and Couples Education.

Scientists who work for the research centre at the University of California San Francisco conducted two large studies which found that older adults who volunteered reaped benefits in their health and well being and lived longer than non volunteers.

A second study found a 44% reduction in early deaths among those who volunteered a lot. It had a greater beneficial effect than exercising four times a week. "Ultimately the process of cultivating positive emotional state through pro-social behaviours and being generous lengthen your life," Dr. Stephen G. Post Ph.D. professor of Bioethics at Case Western Reserve University School of Medicine.

Love is the healing vibration.
Smiling energy is healing energy.
Love yourself.
Affirm yourself.
Act as if.
Carry yourself with love.

GLENDALOUGH

The next morning was sunny and bright. I felt a little brighter too. The previous day of complete rest had greatly helped. It was only then that I realised how right Joanne had been. I hadn't had a proper break in over three years. Since Peter and I had bought the house my annual holidays had been spent decorating it and landscaping the garden, with a lot of help from my friend, Rob. But that was another memory which I didn't want to entertain so I turned on the television for distraction.

It was a rare treat for me to have time to watch morning television, so in effect I was following Tara's instructions without even realising it. I smiled thinking of that. The smile was short lived however when I realised that I was sitting, as usual, with my knees crossed. That was going to be a difficult habit to break. But I was going to do it! I had given up smoking a few years previously. By comparison with that breaking the cross kneed habit should be easy.

The weather forecast following the news was good. It predicted bright, sunny spells, especially in the east. However, cloud from the west was to spread countrywide by nightfall, bringing rain to all areas on Friday. I determined to make hay while the sun shone. I was going to treat myself. I was going to spend the day in Glendalough.

I left Bray via the N11, exited at the slip road which indicated Glendalough and returned to the Wicklow of my childhood.

While the road I had travelled was evidence of man's engineering prowess, the scene opening up before me now was testimony to another type of power. It was at once wild and rugged, yet gentle and soothing. The Sugarloaf Mountain on the left appeared grey, rocky, and foreboding, while the valley on the other side was covered in grass, patterned with wild flowers. It was a sanctuary for feral goats, and a grazing ground for ponies of the travelling community. A statue of the Mother of God stood with open arms in an alcove in the rock. Nothing had changed in over fifteen years. But then how could it? How can you change a mountain? Or the beauty of wild gorse? Or the softness of ferns? Or the exquisite sense of haphazard order which created a scene whose beauty neither artist nor poet could ever exaggerate? The words of the poet, Pádraig Mac Piarais, came to mind.

"The beauty of this world has made me sad.

This beauty that will pass."

At the top of the Long Hill I pulled over and the tears began to flow. Out of nowhere the memories of people and things which I had loved and lost came to mind. Beautiful Lucy who would never again be with me in this or any other special place. Peter, Eddie. The happy atmosphere in my home. My father singing as he shaved. My mother dancing around the kitchen which was filled with the aroma of Lucy's favourite bread. All gone in a puff.

"Give yourself permission to be happy," Tara had advised. I couldn't imagine ever laughing or feeling happy again.

I had been sitting there for what seemed like a short time when there was a knock on the glass. A man dressed in overalls and wellington boots stood smiling in at me. When I obeyed his signal and wound down the window he extended his hand, and while shaking mine firmly, introduced himself as Tom Fields. There were work calluses on his palm.

"Are you alright?" he asked. "Are you having car trouble? I saw you pulled in on my way to the village. When you were still here on my way back I thought maybe you needed a hand."

"No, thank you very much. I'm fine," I protested, although the tears running down my face told a different story.

"Are you sure? If you need a 'phone to call someone you're welcome to use mine."

"No thank you. I'm ok."

"You're not from these parts, are you?"

It was a rhetorical question. I was sure that he knew everyone within a radius of thirty miles.

"I'm on my way to Glendalough. This is the right road, isn't it?" I enquired hoping that by asking directions I was in some small way repaying him for having taken the time to stop.

"Yes straight ahead all the way. Roundwood is the first village you'll come to. Just go straight through, unless of course you want to see a famous film star or musician. There are a lot of them in these parts. They appreciate the peace here, they find it inspirational I believe," he said with a twinkle.

He was a youngish man and had probably spent all his life in this quiet place. Perhaps he'd have liked to have experienced a little of what the stars were trying to escape.

"Go on through Annamoe, and it's straight ahead all the way to Laragh village. Glendalough is about a mile further down the road. It's a very special place. You'll have a lovely day there, stress free," he added knowingly.

Then he got into his little truck and drove off. I had to follow him. Otherwise, I felt sure he'd come back to see what had happened to me.

Like all Irish place names, Glendalough not only identifies a location, but also describes it. Translated into English it becomes the valley of the two lakes. The lakes referred to were formed by glacial erosion. During the last Ice Age, a vast iceberg tore through the Wicklow Mountains decimating all in its path and leaving behind a landscape which bears witness to its journey. Huge stones in the most unlikely settings demonstrate its power. No mortal could have moved them. Many appear as if the only way they could have arrived in their present position is by being dropped from space. Others stand in such precarious situations that one would imagine the slightest wind would topple them over. As well as depositing these erratics the iceberg also tore up large tracts of land as it moved forward, leaving behind deep excavations which became lakes filled with the water streaming down from the snow covered hills. In its wake it also deposited fine golden sea sand. Its discovery, miles from any beach, was a great source of delight for us as children when our father explained how the enormous glacier had stolen it from far-away beaches, and then deposited it here above the highest village in Ireland.

But Glendalough is not just an area of exquisite physical beauty. It is also a spiritual place; the scene of a sixth century monastic city. The near perfect round tower, and the ruins of seven churches, gives testimony to the vibrancy of that settlement. Founded by St. Kevin, this was a centre of prayer and learning during Ireland's Golden Age of Saints and Scholars. Many pilgrims still come to pray to the Saint whose final resting place is said to be marked by the huge Celtic cross at the side of the Cathedral. Legend has it that anyone whose arms can encircle the body of the cross will have their wish granted.

The journey was just as Tom Fields had described it. However, he could have dispensed with all of the details. All he needed to advise was to follow the main road. It wasn't so much a main road, as the only road. Its course had probably remained unchanged over hundreds of years. The countryside all around was still unspoilt, still probably farmed by members of the same families who had farmed it for generations. The few modern houses, invariably situated beside older, more traditional cottages, were, more than likely, new family homes for grown-up children. There was no development as such.

However, while in some ways the site of the Monastic settlement had also remained untouched by time, in other ways it had changed dramatically. But these changes, which were obviously needed to facilitate greater visitor numbers, had been undertaken with great care, and in no way detracted from the great natural beauty of the settlement. The car parks and the interpretive centre were secluded under the shade of native oak and ash trees and were unobtrusive.

As soon as I had parked panic once again threatened to overwhelm me as the realisation struck that I was all alone there. My heart began to race and I could feel my body tense up.

"This can't happen," I said forcefully. "Not here, not now."

"Calm, calm, calm," I repeated as I opened the window and in an effort to distract myself observed the other people in the car park. A couple of hikers took their gear from the boot of their car. When they had laced up their boots, zipped up their jackets and fastened the straps of their rucksacks they set off smiling and with great gusto in the direction of the hills. They looked strong and vigorous. I knew how they felt. I could remember that feeling. I had done the same thing numerous times before. Sitting up straight I repeated, "I'm strong, I'm strong, I'm strong," while visualising the mountains I had climbed and the challenges I had overcome.

"I'm still that person," I said with determination as I got out of the car. But not wishing to tempt fate, I sat down on the first seat I came to. It was snuggled against the wall of the interpretive centre and faced the sun.

With both feet flat on the ground I repeated; "I'm healthy and I'm happy, I'm healthy and I'm happy." Tara said it had worked for her, so it should work for me too. I believed her. I knew that she had returned to good health.

Then connecting with the exquisite beauty which was in evidence everywhere, I smiled and tuned into its magnificence, bringing the emotion of love and appreciation to all the organs and glands in my body as Tara had recommended. When I had smiled away the stress, and sealed the energy at my centre, I began a journey which I had often undertaken as a child.

Once across the bridge I took the road less travelled, turning left, rather than following the sign which pointed towards the lakes. From a distance I could hear my brother Tom's voice,

"What is it Dad?"

"Just wait and see."

"Well where is it? There's nothing here for ages and ages only trees. I'm tired."

"We're nearly there. It's in a secret place. It's hidden away. Not everyone gets to see it."

"Only us?"

"Yes only us, and some other very lucky people."

That motivated Tom, but only just. Reluctantly he followed.

I walked very slowly, seeking out this little gem. I knew it was on this track, but I also remembered that it was hidden from general view. It would be easy to miss. Then, through a gap in the undergrowth, I caught a glimpse of gold shimmering in the sunlight. It was still here after all the years. Using my hands to protect my face and hair I carefully parted the branches of the overhanging trees and reached the oasis of beauty which I had been seeking. Its effect on me was the same as the first time I had laid eyes on it. I automatically inhaled deeply and exhaled an, "Ah," of enchantment.

"It's a Christmas tree," Tom had said transfixed.

"Look Dad. It's a Christmas tree," he had shouted, gleefully dancing in a circle around the source of his delight, all tiredness gone.

"What's it doing here Dad? It's not Christmas." Tom knew Santa didn't come to "our house" in Bray.

"How did it get here? Is it magic?" he had asked.

"It's a prayer tree, Tom. People come here to say their prayers and to put their offerings on the tree," my father had replied lifting him up in his arms so that he could see the decorations more clearly, as we all gazed in wonder at the tree festooned with flowers, rosary beads, medals, coloured ribbons and written petitions.

"Why is the prayer tree here Dad?" Tom had asked.

"It's because it's beside a holy well, a wishing well."

"A wishing well, could it get any better?" I thought as pictures of perfect, long, deep, stone bound wells from my story books came to mind. But this well couldn't have been more different. Practically obscured by lichen and undergrowth it could have easily remained undetected.

We formed a queue. When it was my turn to sit on the little step and to place my hand and my wish in the well, I realised that the water was muddy. But that didn't deter me. Now, once again I sat down, reached in, and made my request. Then rejoining the track I turned in the direction of the lakes. I was now seeking to recapture another enchanted childhood memory; I wanted to sit on the wishing chair.

It must have originally been a huge block of granite, deposited by the same iceberg which was responsible for the creation of this whole valley. However it was now so much more than a lump of inanimate stone. It had a unique personality and beauty. Thanks to the action of wind, rain, ice and snow over centuries it had become a sculpture. A carving of a stool positioned beside a large circular shaped receptacle whose basin was always full of water. Legend has it that this was a place of baptism in the early settlement. Whatever its then function, now it is a giver of dreams. Sitting on the seat I reached over and once again placed my hands in the water. Unlike the last time I had been there, this time they reached. I had grown up!

From the wishing chair I crossed the little wooden bridge which brought me back into the centre of the monastic settlement and to the round tower.

The round tower of Glendalough stands tall and majestic above the ruined city. It is beautiful in its line, structure, and simplicity. The wonder of its construction can so easily be overlooked today. It is only when placed in context that it is possible to appreciate the marvel of this edifice. How did farming people, living in this remote valley fifteen centuries ago, have the expertise to build it? Without scaffolding how did they complete this 30 metre, (98 feet) high construction? Where did they source the building materials? How did they transport them? How long did it take to build? It is bewildering. It is absolutely astounding if viewed in purely human terms. But perhaps I am overlooking a vital ingredient. Perhaps St. Kevin lent a helping hand. Legend would subscribe to this view.

It is said that the workmen employed by St. Kevin promised him that they would get up with the lark and work until sunset every day to complete his settlement in the fastest time possible. In Ireland, in summer time, daylight can begin at 4.30 a.m. and last till 10.30 p.m. The workmen, in deference to their employer, worked as long as there was light in the sky. After some time the Saint noticed that they looked tired and unhappy. When he questioned them they informed him that yes, he was right. They were exhausted because they had no sooner gone to sleep than the larks were wakening them up with their dawn chorus. As soon as the Saint was made aware of this he spoke to the birds.

"*Beannacht Dé oraibh agus míle buíochas díobh as ucht an cheol binn a canann sibh.*

Mar is éol díobh gráim sibh, agus tá fíor fáilte róibh anseo I gconaí.

Is breá an rud é dúiseacht gach maidin agus ceol aoibhinn ag seinnt.

Ach tá na fir an tuirseach ar maidin taréis dóibh bheith ag obair an lá ar fad, mar sin impím oraibh, más'é bhur dtoil é, gan canadh anseo go dtí go bhfuil an ghrian go hard sa spéir. Nuair atá an obair thart beidh gach rud mar a bhí."

[God bless you and a thousand thanks for your sweet music. As you know I love you and you are always welcome here. It is wonderful to waken each morning to the sound of beautiful music. But the men are very tired after working all day long, so for that reason I ask you please not to sing over Glendalough until the sun is high in the sky. When the work is completed all will be as before.]

The birds took no exception to his request. They knew his kindness to them. When the winter was cruel, which it often was in those high hills, he fed them by hand. So they were happy to accede to his request. Perhaps he had helped the building in other ways as well!

Unlike the numerous visitors marvelling at the tower it was not the focus of my attention. I had come to seek help. Standing as close as possible to the large Celtic cross, said to mark St. Kevin's last resting place, I tried unsuccessfully to wrap my arms around it. But no matter how much I stretched, my fingers failed to touch. I made a wish anyway.

The sun was still warm on my face as I opened my eyes and returned to reality. My reverie was over. Next time I'd walk it for real; that was my fervent prayer.

When I checked my watch it was three fifteen, and I felt hungry.

In the bright dining room of The Glendalough Hotel, looking out on a restful green vista, I enjoyed every mouthful of my steak and Guinness pie. Then I returned to Bray feeling exhausted. It had been a very emotional day.

RELAPSE

As predicted the following day was dark, dull, and wet. That's the nature and beauty of the Irish climate. Unrestricted by season, it is as possible to have a beautiful, summer-like day in March, as a wintry one in June. I was happy that I had made the most of the previous day's sunshine. After breakfast, armed with the paper, which Marie at reception handed me with a big smile, I drove to the harbour.

Bray's harbour is tiny. In summer it provides mooring for a small number of boats. But, much more significantly, all year round it teems with wild life. It is home to more than a hundred swans, numerous ducks, geese, and countless sea gulls. The inhabitants of the town have taken this resident wildlife to their hearts. Every day a constant stream of people come to feed them. The swans are so tame that they wade out of the water to be hand-fed by their admirers, and to the delight of the children bread thrown upwards produces a spectacular air display from the ever hungry sea gulls.

However that day the harbour was empty of both human and wild life. I wondered where all the birds could be. Perhaps they knew from experience that there would be no free meals today. Perhaps they realised that the rain would deter their supporters from coming to feed them. Perhaps they were out at sea or further up the river foraging.

The sky was low. Its greyness was reflected in the water so that sky and sea merged seamlessly on the horizon. The whiteness of the foam on the top of the breakers contrasted with the steely grey waves. It was beautiful. I pushed back the driver's seat and made myself comfortable. Then I took out St. Paul's letter to the Corinthians and began to read:

Love is gentle.
Love is kind.
Love is not jealous or boastful.
It is not arrogant or rude.
Love does not insist on its own way.
It is not resentful.
It does not rejoice in wrong, but rejoices in the truth.
Love believes all things.
Love bears all things.
Hopes all things.
Endures all things.
Charity never falls away, whether prophesies shall be made void,
or tongues shall cease, or knowledge be destroyed.
And now these three remain, faith, hope and charity and
the greatest of these is charity.

I reread it a few times. Each time I was amazed by its forcefulness and certainty. Nothing was anything without love. And the love which St. Paul alluded to was obviously so much more than the love of romantic songs and stories. It was not exclusive or confined, it was all embracing. I read again:

Love is patient.
Love is kind.
I stopped and repeated those lines.
Love is patient.
Love is kind.

"Internalise this," Tara had advised. "Follow the directions in your life. Start with yourself. Begin by being kind and gentle with yourself."

There in the safe environment of the car, snug and protected from the elements, and with no human presence in sight, it was somehow easy to contemplate. With my eyes closed, I examined my conscience to determine in what way I had been less than gentle or kind to myself. It didn't take long for an answer to emerge. Of late I had become very self-critical. In both my professional and private life I had taken to blaming myself for everything that I perceived to be wrong.

"Be as kind to yourself as you are to the person you love most in the whole world," Tara had advised.

I thought of my friend Louise. She also had a very responsible job; teaching in a large city centre school. If she was agonising over something, or if she was blaming herself for everything that went wrong in her school, I'd use gentleness and kindness to assure her that she had done all that she could possibly have done. From now on I was going to treat myself in the same way.

Then out of the blue an image of one of my patients came to mind. Alan Price had been attending the surgery for about three years. He suffered from respiratory problems and had been hospitalised with pneumonia on two occasions. I had marked him down as another one of my failures. I recalled the last time I had seen him.

"No better," was his reply when I had enquired how he was. "That medication you prescribed is useless," he'd continued. "Is there anything else you can give me? There must be something else you can do."

Recalling the incident even then, weeks and miles distant, still caused me to cringe. I interpreted his inability to breathe as a reflection on me, on my ineffectiveness as a doctor.

"You're useless," I'd tell myself when he or any other long-term patient left the surgery. But now, with the eye of gentleness, I looked at his case from a perspective I had never looked from before.

"Maybe, you're not the problem," I found myself saying. "Alan is still smoking, despite all the warnings you have given him. Regardless of the anti-smoking literature and the research findings you have made available to him, he continues to compromise his breathing. His illness is not a result of your failure, but of his," I said aloud.

Then I repeated what I had just said.

"His illness is not a result of your failure, but of his." That was an extremely liberating conclusion.

Then I thought of Helen Murray, another long-term patient.

"Oh doctor I'm dying," was her usual response to my greeting. "I've no energy. I can't go from here to there without having to sit down to catch my breath."

"Have you noticed any improvement since I changed your medication?"

"No doctor, it's useless. I'm still the same."

"Are you following the diet plan which I gave you? Have you cut down on your food intake and started the exercise programme I suggested?"

"I'm trying," was her constant reply.

According to Helen she had been trying for years. But there was no obvious sign of this. She was still overweight; a factor which was definitely contributing to her condition.

"That's not your fault," some intelligence deep within me cried out. "You're not responsible for someone else's behaviour or lethargy. You're not to blame for things that are outside your control. You can't stop your patients smoking, or overeating, or drinking to excess no matter how much you want to. Their lifestyle is their choice. You're not to blame. It's not your fault." The voice of gentleness and kindness had spoken again.

"You're not to blame. It's not your fault," the words formed a jingle in my head. I gave them free rein. That's what Tara would have suggested. I was changing the record. I was being positive. I was being gentle and kind.

As I was driving out of the harbour two figures emerged from the gates of the sailing club. They were huddled closely together under an umbrella which had obviously been battered by the strong winds. Since the rain was relentless I stopped to offer them a lift before recognising them as Mike and Carol.

"Hop in," I said. "I thought I was the only one here. As they'd say in Mullingar, have you no home to go to?"

"No," Carol replied from the back of the car.

When I looked in the mirror to smile at what I thought was an amusing reply I realised that she was in deadly earnest. I got the distinct impression that I had hit a nerve. So I resolved to say nothing else.

"It's the house with the swing in the garden," Mike said by way of identification when we pulled into the estate. As I turned the car in the driveway they let themselves into the granny flat at the side of the house. Two young children were looking out the downstairs window and waving at them.

"Dreadful day," Marie said as she handed me my key. "It's such a pity the rain came. There's not much you can do on a day like this."

"I spent it at the harbour," I informed her.

"Were you in the Harbour Bar? You know it has been voted the best bar in the world?"

"No, I just stayed in the car and watched the waves."

"It's well worth a visit; you never know who you'd meet there."

We both laughed at her inference.

Back in the room I made myself some tea and sat down, cup in hand, observing the few hardy souls braving the elements. They seemed to be walking to the beat of the tune still playing in my head. "It's not your fault. You're not to blame." Then they were joined by many others marching to the same beat; Carol Flynn and her children who were constantly plagued by colds, flu, and whatever was going.

"But they won't eat fruit and vegetables for me doctor."

"It's not your fault. You're not to blame."

Paul Egan, who suffered from depression.

"No, I wouldn't go to the men's shed. No, I wouldn't go to the day care centre. No I don't want you to organise someone to call to me. No I don't need company. No, no, no."

"It's not your fault. You're not to blame."

Then I saw Lucy. Immediately the terror struck. Grabbing my stomach first it then travelled to my throat strangling the breath out of me. I could feel the blockage in my windpipe growing, leaving me once again gasping for air. It became larger and larger, a big obstacle squeezed into a very confined space. It pained me. I collapsed onto the bed and lay there shaking, knowing that I was no match for it; that my resistance to it would only result in it increasing its ferocity. It was a tenacious enemy. I just had to let it run its course. Closing my eyes I tried disempowering it by denying it any attention. Desperately trying to ignore the uproar that was occurring in my body with as much concentration as I could muster I repeated; "I'm calm, I'm calm, I'm calm."

Despite my best efforts it refused to dissipate. Using every atom of my energy as its own it shook, squeezed, pummelled, and punched. It was as if many agents were now working together to batter me to oblivion. I was helpless. I could feel the life draining from me, but was too feeble to protest. I capitulated. There was no other way. Only when I was totally devastated did it pass. Once again its victory was absolute, leaving me completely powerless, defeated and distraught. Totally wrecked, and robbed of the new shoots of confidence and joy which I had just begun to experience, I lay spent out on the bed. In the calm I noticed the silence. It had also stolen my jingle. That was something I couldn't allow to happen. I needed to hear that refrain again. I needed to allow it to seep through me until it became part of me, until it was so ingrained in my psyche that I would feel strong enough to withstand any attack on my competence. I needed that jingle. Very deliberately I restarted it;

"You're not to blame.

It's not your fault."

Then a gentle voice, completely outside my control, whispered,

"You did your best"

"You did your best."

As usual, it took me two days to recover from the onslaught. Physically I was exhausted, but that wasn't the worst part. My confidence had again taken a hammering. For those two days I was afraid to leave the confines of the hotel. I was scared to go out in case I would suffer a relapse. There in the hotel I felt safe. I knew that Marie would look after me if I needed help.

Despite the set back however, I had to stay positive. That was my only hope. That's what Tara had advised, and she was living proof of the effectiveness of her strategies. Consciously during the days that followed I filled my head with my mantras. Sometimes one would play to the exclusion of the other two. Sometimes the three of them wrestled for attention at the same time. I just gave them permission and they played.

"You're not to blame.

It's not your fault.

You did your best."

As the days went on I reduced them down to one;

"You do your best." That was it! I liked the sound of that.

AIR

At 7.45 p.m. on Tuesday I was the only person in room two of the community centre. Fearing that nobody else was going to turn up, panic gripped me.

"What am I going to do?" I asked myself. "I'll be the total focus of her attention." When the implications of that thought struck me I rushed towards the exit. As I reached for the handle the door swung open. Thinking that Tara was about to catch me trying to escape my heart nearly stopped. I was greatly relieved when it was David who came in.

He nodded in response to my greeting, and when we had placed the chairs in a circle we both sat down in the exact positions which we had occupied on the previous Wednesday; directly across from one another. That suited me fine. I was able to observe him, to monitor any change in his appearance. Unbelievably, he had definitely cleaned up; the signature slobber from last week was no longer visible on the front of his sweater. In fact both his top and pants looked spotless. But his hair and beard were still badly in need of attention.

The rest of the group arrived just before Tara, who came in as the clock on the wall showed 8 p.m. exactly. Once again she looked wonderful in a straight, knee length, red dress. Discreet diamond studs matched the pendant which hung on a gold chain around her neck. In her case less was always more. Her style was simple but chic.

She greeted each of us by name and asked if there were any questions based on the previous week's session. When it was obvious that no one was going to contribute, she leaned forward on her chair, smiled, and was just about to speak when we were distracted by the sound of a yawn, followed by a very loud sigh. It was Liz, seated on Tara's right, who now became the focus of our attention. Her face reddened, and she became flustered and embarrassed.

"Oh, excuse me. Oh I'm very sorry. I'm just exhausted today," she stammered, her hands trembling and a look of distress and helplessness on her face.

I hoped that she wasn't going to have a panic attack, afraid that it would cause me to panic as well. But for all that I couldn't resist looking at her.

"Had you a very hard day Liz?" Tara asked in a gentle voice, reaching over and taking hold of her hand.

Liz shook her head.

"I'm exhausted every day," she said, straining to keep the emotion from her voice. "It doesn't seem to matter how early I go to bed, or how much sleep I get." Her tears weren't too far away now. "I'm exhausted all the time. I'm nearly at breaking point," she said reaching for her bag and taking out a packet of tissues. "I'm just at the end of my tether."

We all listened in an uncomfortable silence. Then, as if a boil had been lanced, all her anxieties came pouring out, not in a controlled, free flowing way; rather in a convulsion of phrases and single words, depending on the frequency, and the ferocity of the sobs which she tried unsuccessfully to control.

"I have no energy. Everything is a chore. Last week, I couldn't even treat myself to something beautiful, as you suggested, because I was afraid it would leave me totally exhausted and I'd have to take to the bed," she sobbed. "The children are out of control. I don't have the energy to correct or discipline them." Her head sank lower onto her chest. "Now they just ignore me. They feel they can do as they like. It's all my fault." Her tears streamed down her face.

"I'm afraid Frank will leave," she said gasping for breath, as if the thought of that happening had her fighting for her life.

Her weeping became so intense now, that despite many efforts to continue speaking, she was unable to do so. She looked so pathetic sitting there sobbing and shredding the tissues she had been fiddling with. Her pain was palpable. Eventually she continued in a barely audible voice.

"I wouldn't blame him if he did. The thought of facing me, constantly complaining about how tired I feel, must be agonising. He's the one who should be tired. He leaves home at 6 a.m. and drives hundreds of miles a day. But then I've been under unimaginable stress too," she added, as in a gesture of complete surrender to the despair which gripped her she shrank down into the chair. Her shoulders curved inwards and her head dropped.

Tara continued to hold her hand. I just wanted to leave the room. I was feeling distressed, and my breath grew shallow and uneven. Everyone sat with their eyes downcast. Nobody spoke or moved.

"Oh please, I'm so sorry, I'm really sorry," she apologised, hoisting herself up in the chair and breaking the silence. While her words were obviously intended for the group, she addressed them directly to Tara.

"There's no need to apologize Liz. You have just very nicely highlighted the importance of tonight's strategy," Tara said in her usual calm, reassuring voice.

"It's all confidential isn't it?" Liz asked anxiously, as if Tara's comment hadn't registered with her. "I don't want anyone to hear what I said. I'd feel so ashamed."

"Yes, everything that happens here is strictly confidential," Tara assured her. "But there is nothing to be ashamed of Liz. You have just outlined a difficulty which most people encounter at some stage in their lives. You are experiencing low energy as a result of bad breathing habits. It's a feature of modern living. It's pandemic. The speed of life results in us rushing everything, including our breathing; and the stresses of life disrupt what should be its slow even pattern. And our automatic instinct, to try to protect ourselves from the pollution in cities and air conditioned buildings, causes us to take quick shallow breaths, just enough to get us by. This wreaks havoc on us. We are all victims of it. The problem is widespread. Chances are that you are not the only person in the group with this dilemma."

I glanced in Tara's direction to see if she was looking at me, but Liz was still the focus of her attention. She looked pitiful. Since her outburst, it was as if she had shed the outer façade which had given her the appearance of a fairly average functioning person. Now, divested of that, she looked exactly as she really was; a tired and frightened young woman.

"Tonight we are going to concentrate on powerful, effective methods to breathe properly," Tara continued, taking some photocopied material from her bag. "We are going to discover simple ways to breathe which will allow us to access the powerful vibrations which are all around us. As I said last week the whole focus of this course is to tap into positive energy."

That magic word, energy. The very mention of it had an immediate positive effect on me. I sat up straighter and gave her my full attention.

"If I were to say to you that the most important ingredient in energy production is free, painless, and readily available, wherever you are, and whenever you need it, what would you say?" Tara asked.

"I'd say, please tell us what it is," Liz answered without any hesitation.

Tara nodded. "The basis of our whole energy production system is a chemical called Adenosine Triphosphate," she said, "and here is the beauty of it, its most vital component is oxygen. So for as long as we are capable of breathing, we have the power to increase our energy levels."

"But I breathe all the time," Liz insisted, "and I have absolutely no energy."

"But there's breathing and there's effective breathing," Tara said once again turning to Liz. "How many times did you actually sit down to-day Liz?" she asked. Liz looked at her in amazement, as if the question was a ridiculous one.

"I can't remember."

"Well, was it four or five times?"

"I sat down for my lunch, and my tea. I never sit down for my breakfast. I'm always rushing to get the children ready for school. Why do you ask?"

"Because the kind of breath necessary to provide our bodies with sufficient oxygen to power them is a deep breath, and that takes a little time. But because our lifestyles have become so frantic and hurried, we tend to rush our breathing. We don't take time to breathe. In fact we seldom, if ever, think of our breathing. And worse still, when we become stressed out from all the rushing around, we actually tend not to breathe at all."

"I know I do that," Liz volunteered. "When there's a problem with the children, or any kind of emergency, I actually hold my breath and stop breathing."

"Me too," I added, remembering how sometimes, during my panic attacks, I was literally afraid to breathe for fear of making things worse. I consciously tightened myself up, and tried to close down all my bodily functions, so as not to exacerbate what was happening.

"I can't explain where that reflex of not breathing when in danger comes from," Tara said, "but it is absolutely the wrong strategy. When the body is under stress its requirement for oxygen skyrockets, so that is precisely the time when we need to breathe most. Both the brain, and the heart, the body's most vital organs, have huge oxygen requirements. If in times of trauma, they are trying to function on an inadequate supply, mistakes, accidents, or even death may result. To make a conscious effort to breathe when under stress, when oxygen is most important to us, is imperative. So from now on I urge you to be aware of your breathing at all times. The quality of your life, and the state of your health, is dependent on the amount of oxygen in your system. If you feel challenged in any way, be assured that increasing the level of oxygen in your blood will bring about an amazing improvement in your condition. All we need do to feel better, is to breathe more efficiently and deeply."

She made it all sound so easy. It was as if no matter what the problem, there was a simple solution. Her next sentence illustrated that quality. "It will take only a few minutes to breathe properly, but the effects will be obvious almost instantly," she assured us.

Yet again she stressed the importance of oxygen in our lives by reminding us that we can survive without food for weeks, without water for days, but a lack, or even a restricted supply of oxygen, can result in brain damage.

"The brain requires more oxygen than any other organ," she repeated. "If it doesn't get enough, the result is mental sluggishness, negative thoughts, depression and eventually vision and hearing decline. Old people, and those whose arteries are clogged, get irritated very quickly and become senile and vague, because the supply of oxygen to the brain is reduced. And children who have insufficient oxygen for just a few minutes at birth, suffer irreversible brain damage," she said. "Oxygen is so vital to the body that we are actually fitted with a warning signal to alert us to dangerously low levels," she continued. "We yawn and sigh. And when that happens, not only is it a sign that our oxygen is low, but it also a signal that our energies are depleted, and that it's time to breathe in earnest."

All eyes turned to Liz, who, strangely enough, looked a little better. She was sitting up straighter and was totally focused on Tara. Perhaps, like me, the very mention of the word energy had had a positive effect on her.

"I can't believe that something as basic and simple as breathing properly will help me," she said turning to look at Tara. "But I pray that it's true. You're the only person who has given me a ray of hope. I was beginning to despair of ever feeling well again."

"You'll be truly amazed at the difference you will feel when your body is properly oxygenated. It's our most essential requirement. It is the source of our vitality," Tara said smiling brightly.

"It will take more than breathing to help me," Sean said under his breath. His agitation was palpable. I felt tense.

Mike who was sitting beside him and had obviously heard him broke the silence.

"You've just reminded me of an experience I had as a kid," he said addressing Tara. "I was very interested in Kung Fu and the martial arts. Our club organised an outing to Dublin to see the fighting Shaolin Temple Monks from the Henan Province of China, who were on a fund raising tour of Europe. They were absolutely amazing, performing super-human feats. Some of them even appeared to fly. But my abiding memory of that night was the comment of the narrator. As if aware of the question which everyone in the theatre was posing, he said: "The secret is in the breath. The breath is the source of all power."

Tara nodded her agreement.

"I'm not promising that you'll be able to break concrete blocks with your hand, or that you'll feel no pain splitting timber with your head, but you will definitely feel much more energetic and well when you start to breathe effectively. In fact," she continued, "some of the world's leading researchers have conducted studies which prove the ability of oxygen to eradicate our deadliest illnesses. Dr. Otto Warburg, the director of The Max Planck Institute, won the Nobel Prize for Medicine in 1931 for his work in this area. His research showed that normal healthy cells became malignant when deprived of oxygen. In his acceptance address he stated that the cure for cancer would cost governments virtually nothing, if people were taught to breathe properly. There are also many other erudite studies which illustrate the power of oxygen to combat disease," she said passing around the course handouts. "I have included the titles of some of them with tonight's notes. I hope they will be of interest to anyone who wishes to read further on this topic."

As the handouts were being passed around she again emphasized the benefits of effective breathing.

"When I started to breathe properly I felt I'd tapped into a magic formula," she said. "The increase in oxygen levels brings immediate vitality to the stressed organs, and also burns up waste products which the lymph system will carry away. A clean body is like a clean engine, powerful and energy efficient."

When she stopped speaking we all turned our attention to the sheets which she had passed around. The first one indicated that a proper life-enhancing breath should be slow and even. That the best position for deep breathing was lying on a rug, or mat, with the knees bent, and the feet turned slightly outwards, about eight inches apart.

The arms were to be placed by the sides, with the palms turned upwards. Then while inhaling deeply through the nose one was to imagine filling the body with all manner of good things; new energy, love, light, laughter, beauty, and health. The stomach was to expand outwards to its full capacity. When it was filled with air the chest was to expand sideways. When the whole body was full, one was to exhale through the mouth expelling all negativity, stress, worry, sadness, and illness. This constituted one deep breath. A little red asterisk informed us that the breaths which are exhaled forcefully through the mouth are called cleansing breaths.

Because oxygen is so powerful, it was advised that no more than four of these deep breaths should be taken at a time. The next sentence really struck me as very important, and yet it was something that had never occurred to me before. It emphasized the body's inability to store oxygen and consequently the need to replenish its supply at regular intervals throughout the day.

"Of course," I thought! "That makes sense. Just as it is necessary to replenish our food and liquid supplies as the body uses them up, so its oxygen must also be renewed throughout the day as the organs utilise it." It was so obvious, when it was pointed out!

About sixty deep breaths a day was given as the target to aim for. But we were advised to start slowly, by taking three or four at intervals throughout the day, so as not to overload the lymphatic system with toxins which the newly energised body would throw off. The following revitalizing breaths were also recommended. They were performed in a standing position with the arms outstretched at shoulder level.

The first one involved taking a deep breath in through the nose, and while retaining it to move the arms out to the sides, and then back to the starting position several times, before dropping them while exhaling forcefully, widely opening the mouth. The second one suggested taking a deep breath in through the nose, and while holding it to circle the arms like a windmill, before dropping them and exhaling as before. For the next breath the fingertips were placed on the shoulders. The breath was inhaled deeply through the nose, and while retaining it the elbows were joined on the chest, and then moved apart several times. The exhalation was to be forceful, through a widely opened mouth. The final exercise also involved retained the breath for a few seconds during which time the blood would have time to re-oxygenate. The in-breath was through the nose, and the out-breath through the mouth in the ratio of 1:4:3. I was just about to ask for clarification when Liz spoke. "Can I just see if I have that last one right?" she asked.

"Certainly."

"If I inhale for a count of 2, I hold my breath for a count of 8 and exhale for a count of 6. Is that right?"

"That is the ideal to aim for," Tara said emphasising not to strain, rather to build up to this quota over time, and to make haste slowly.

Then on her instruction we sat up straight with both feet flat on the floor. While breathing in through the nose we imagined filling our tummies to capacity with all good things. Then expanding the ribcage sideways we filled our chest cavity, after which we exhaled through the mouth expelling all stress, illness and negativity. When we had repeated the exercise a few times I definitely felt energized. In fact, it felt as if the energy in the room had changed.

"Remember these are exercises," Tara informed us. "It is not suggested that you breathe like this all the time. Normally one breathes in and out through the nose. This ensures that the air is heated as it is inhaled which prevents cold air being sucked into the lungs causing stress and coughing, particularly for asthma sufferers. The hair follicles in the nose also act as filters cleaning the air as it is drawn in.

But the deep breathing exercises will automatically ensure that your normal breathing will improve and your energy levels also. Of all the strategies I found the deep breathing was the one which produced the most immediate effect," she said. "As soon as I started to breathe deeply, at regular intervals throughout the day, I noticed a dramatic change, not only in my physical body, but in my mood, my thoughts and my whole being. And if you need an added incentive to take the time out to breathe let me read you this," she said taking a sheet of green paper from her bag. "It's a flyer advertising oxygen bars, which came through my letter box a few years ago. I'm not sure if they are still operating. But I believe it is better to take our oxygen in the great out-doors e.g. at the beach, or in a forest, or park, or any unpolluted area. In that way we can be assured that the air we are inhaling is suited to us and that all its elements are properly balanced and in the correct proportions."

Then turning her attention to the flyer she read:

"Oxygen is known to slow the ageing process.
To strengthen the immune system.
To eliminate fungi, bacteria and yeast.
To promote health and healing.
To improve athletic performance.
To improve skin condition.
To minimise the appearance of wrinkles."

Then, while replacing the oxygen bar advertisement in her bag, she asked if anyone had ever experienced a shock from a supermarket trol-ley, or their car door. We all nodded and murmured, "Yes".

"These shocks are an indication of an energy blockage," she said. "The following breathing exercise will ground the body, just as an earth wire grounds an electrical appliance. It will encourage the energy to flow uninterrupted from the crown of the head to the soles of the feet, preventing any obstructions, and ensuring a continuous flow of new, healing power."

When we were all standing she directed us to place the feet at shoulder distance apart with the hands on the tummy. Then, with the eyes closed, we breathed deeply in through the nose and out through the mouth. After a few of these breaths she instructed us to bring our attention to our feet, ensuring that our weight was evenly distributed, and that we had established a firm connection with the floor. While breathing in through the nose we visualised the breath flowing down our bodies to the ground. Then we imagined expelling all the tiredness and strain as we breathed out. This type of grounding breath was very beneficial in times of stress, she explained, since it takes the build-up of pressure from the head, and puts us in touch with the earth, with reality, and hence restores balance.

"Can I check if I have that right please?" Liz asked.

Tara nodded.

While Liz still looked shattered I got the distinct feeling that her mood had lifted. I couldn't quite put my finger on the difference in her, but she seemed more purposeful as she repeated almost verbatim what Tara had just said.

"There's also another breath which I'd like to demonstrate and which I recommend you incorporate into your day," Tara continued. "It will prove very beneficial to anyone whose work is stressful. Standing once again with the feet shoulder distance apart, breathe in deeply through the nose. This time the focus of your attention is your centre. Feel the tummy undulate with your breath. The energy that you are now bringing to this area will nourish it and awaken the intelligence at your core, the intuitive intelligence, the gut feeling. By establishing communication with this intelligence we can trust it to direct us. Then when you have filled your system with new oxygen, exhale all stress, anxiety, and fear through the mouth."

When Tara had finished speaking Liz talked us through the procedure again. She was very obviously intent on increasing her oxygen supply.

"Remember the brain has the biggest oxygen requirement," Tara said before the class ended. "So these exercises are particularly important for people who have sedentary jobs, or people who are working indoors in air-conditioned rooms. In these situations the brain can become oxygen starved, because the body, aware that the air it is breathing is not fresh, takes only shallow breaths supplying it with the barest minimum to function. In order to maintain life the brain must be supplied with oxygen. When there is a limited supply it will use most of what is available resulting in a lack to other body parts causing tired-ness, irritability, stress, and disturbed sleep. The combined effect of this is that the immune system is compromised and susceptible to colds and flu. If this situation continues for some time more serious illnesses like cancer, heart disease, and organ malfunctions can occur. So during the coming week please add the deep breathing exercises to the strat-egies recommended at last week's session," she said before wishing us a very good night.

In The Tea Cup Liz sat with Rose and me. Sean was across from us. His expression was dour.

"I hope my problem can be as easily solved as Tara suggested," Liz said as soon as we sat down. "I must say I am encouraged by what I've heard, and especially by her reference to the work of Dr. Warburg," she said consulting the handout. "His research has given me hope."

I was glad that Liz was so intent on the course notes that she didn't notice Sean's dismissive look. I wondered, not for the first time, why he came at all. It was so obvious from his body language that he was totally unimpressed and bored by the whole thing. He was so full of anger, just like a tinder box ready to explode. I wondered if his wife had left him, or if he had lost his job, or if something even worse, some-thing I didn't want to contemplate had happened to him; something as devastating as losing Lucy. And if that was the case I couldn't blame him for his scepticism. Balanced against that pain the simple common sense strategies which Tara was advocating seemed futile. I'd have felt exactly the same except that I had a huge advantage over Sean; I knew that the strategies had worked for Tara. That's why I was there.

"I hope I won't be disappointed again," Liz said. Then her voice broke with emotion and her eyes filled with tears. We sat in an uncom-fortable silence for a few moments. I was afraid to comment in case it would upset her again. I just sat there wishing I was somewhere else.

After a while Rose said, "I hope I'm not interfering Liz, but if you don't mind, perhaps, from the benefit of my forty years teaching expe-rience, I could give you a few pointers on dealing with the children. They seem to be draining you."

Liz nodded unenthusiastically, prompted by politeness I felt, more than interest.

"I have always found that the very best way to manage children's behaviour is to spend time playing with them; having fun," Rose started enthusiastically. "I wouldn't have the energy," Liz cut in immediately.

"That's the beauty of it," Rose continued undaunted. "You don't have to do anything, just be there. The reason why most children misbehave is because it gets them the notice they crave. But if they know that they will have your undivided attention for a definite period every day they won't need to act up, and you won't have to expend your energy correcting and giving out to them."

At that moment Liz looked the most unlikely candidate imaginable to engage with children in play. It seemed as if the simple act of sitting was draining her. Rose was obviously thinking along the same lines.

"I know it sounds more trouble than it's worth, but believe me Liz, if you set aside a definite playtime for them it will pay dividends," she said squeezing her hand reassuringly. "And just one more thing, every day at some stage, perhaps when you go in to wish them good night, try to spend some time on a one-to-one basis with each child. Have a chat; see if there's anything worrying them. This will also help build up a good bond. That's the whole idea of the exercise, to build up a positive loving relationship."

I felt that there were many other hints which Rose could have added, but sensing Liz's exhaustion she stopped there.

"See how you get on with those suggestions Liz," she said. "And by the way, I would happily babysit for you anytime, if you give me a little notice. I'm generally free." In response to this kindness Liz's tears started to flow again. She was definitely in a very fragile state.

Back at the hotel I read the following information in the notes which Tara had given us:

Scientific evidence of the importance of oxygen for good health:

Fritz Albert Lipman, winner of the 1953 Nobel Prize for medicine, described oxygen as the main energy transfer for the cell: defining it as an essential ingredient for most of the body cells to make energy. He declared that the brain and the heart cannot survive without oxygen. "Initially a lack of oxygen affects organs but with time the damage is irreversible, within minutes in the case of the brain," he said.

"Cancer is a condition within the body where the oxidation has become so depleted that the body cells have degenerated beyond control. The body has become so overloaded with toxins that is sets up a tumour mass to harbour these poisons and remove them from the general activity within the body."
Dr. Wendell Hendricks of the Hendricks' Research Foundation.

Dr. Harry Goldblatt writing in The Journal of Experimental Medicine 1953 described his experiments which found that a species of rat, never known to develop malignant growths, did so when their oxygen supply was reduced.

An editorial in the Journal of The Royal Society of Medicine suggests that fast shallow breathing can cause fatigue, sleep disorders; anxiety, stomach upsets, heart burn, gas, chest pains.

The germ is nothing. The terrain is everything. Louis Pasteur.

At the bottom of the sheet Tara had summarized that evening's class:
Oxygen is the body's most essential requirement.
Oxygen can prevent cancer, heart disease, and other serious illnesses.
Oxygen is vital for energy production.
Deep breaths nourish and cleanse.
The body cannot store oxygen. Replenish it throughout the day.

STRESS RELEASING BREATH
Identify the area of stress or discomfort.
Bring your awareness to it. If possible place the hands on it. Breathe deeply through the nose. Direct the breath to that area, and breathe out forcibly through the mouth.
Repeat until you feel more relaxed.

As soon as the 'phone rang I felt sure that it was Rob. There had never been a time when Rob hadn't been in my life. He was my best friend. Born in the same month, and living in the same village, we went through school together sharing all the significant events; christenings, first communions, confirmations.

Rob was unique. He could liven up any occasion with a song or story, invariably a funny one, even if he was the butt of the joke. He had the rare ability of being able to laugh at himself. Laughter was his essence and his constant companion. His prolific memory was filled with happy, funny incidents. He was a party to some of these happenings by virtue of his work as a gardener. He was well-known, not only to his clients, but also to those engaged in any ancillary business connected with gardening. He knew the owners of all the garden centres for miles around, the people who repaired garden machinery, the people who sold garden fencing, the people who worked at making wrought iron railings and gates. Rob knew just about everybody in the area, and they knew him. Through all these contacts he had a finger on the pulse, and was clued into everything that was happening in the vicinity.

The time he spent in the local pub, cultivating his skill as a connoisseur of fine whiskey, also added to his repertoire of hilarious incidents. You could bet that the group laughing loudest and longest was in his company. Even the sadness of death was eased by his presence. At wakes, or after funerals, he would regale families with stories of their dearly departed. I have seen people shed tears of laughter in the room where their loved one was laid out as Rob entertained them with stories of their lives. I have also noticed that after those tears the bereaved seemed to stand taller and prouder. Consequently Rob was always most welcome at these functions. We, his brothers Jack, and Liam, and his sister Nora, my brother Tom, and Lucy, who adored him, named him Rent a Wake. The name was conferred on him in the spirit of genuine admiration. We didn't know anyone else who could do what he did. He was aware of his moniker. As expected he just laughed.

His second nickname was conferred in respect of another gift which he displayed in a very different setting. We, the same company, called him Tracker. Tracker was like a homing pigeon. This innate talent was obvious from the very beginning when as children we explored first the fields, and later the hills around us. Despite everything, bad weather, fog, boggy terrain, flooded rivers, Tracker always found a way home. Over the years the gang had become smaller and smaller, marriage, emigration, and death, had claimed the others. Now Tracker and I were the only ones free to walk the hills. It was a pursuit that we both loved. But, of course, like all other enjoyments in my life, it too had been taken away. I hadn't been walking with Tracker for some weeks.

"How are you Rachael?" he asked when I finally answered the cell phone after a frantic search. It took me a little while to extricate it from between the cushion and the frame of the chair where I had been sitting the day before when Louise had rang. I had hoped she was calling to say that she was coming to visit me in Bray, but one of her children had chickenpox, so that was the end of that.

"Are you ok?"

"Ok thanks Rob. How are you doing?" I enquired, very aware that he was also devastated by Lucy's death. "Have you been walking lately?"

"Yes, Shay and I went to Westport at the weekend. We climbed Croagh Patrick. It was great. We were very lucky, the cloud cleared when we got to the top and we could see all the islands in Clew Bay. It was fantastic, the best view I've ever had."

"Are you going back on Reek Sunday?" I asked, referring to the last Sunday in July when thousands of people, from all over Ireland and beyond, gather to climb this mountain where legend has it Saint Patrick prayed and fasted.

"Yes, I'm doing a sponsored climb for the lifeboats."

Rob's sponsorship of the lifeboats was so typical of him. The nearest sea to us was about sixty five miles, (104 km.) away.

"How about this coming weekend Rachael? Are you game for a hike? It might do you good. It seems ages since we were out together.

I thought maybe we'd try Galtee Mór again. The last time we were there was a bit of a disaster wasn't it? All that climbing and nothing for it."

"Yes, it was disappointing all right," I agreed, remembering the dense fog which had obscured our view from the top of the mountain.

"This weekend should be better. The forecast is good, with plenty of dry bright weather promised. What do you think?"

"I won't be home at the weekend Rob. I'm in Bray. Sorry about that."

"No problem, I can come to the mountain Rachael," I could hear the smile in his voice. "I'd enjoy a walk in the Wicklow Hills," he continued. "It would make a change; new horizons."

"I'm not really sure Rob. It's been so long since I was hiking. I might not be up to it."

"No problem. If you can't walk it, we'll drive it," he replied in classic Rob fashion. "Actually there's an interesting article about Wicklow in this month's "Hiker's World." I'll bring it with me."

"Ok Rob. Which day suits you best?"

"What about Saturday, is that ok for you?"

"Saturday is fine."

"Great, I look forward to it Rachael. We can catch up then."

When I had hung up I felt better, more positive somehow. Rob always had that effect on me. He was a great friend and I was very lucky to know him.

THE WICKLOW WAY

Rob arrived at 7.50 a.m. on Saturday morning. I was on the steps of the hotel watching out for him in case he had any problem with the directions I'd given him on the 'phone.

"Great to see you," he said. "We're blessed with the day. There's no rain forecast for the weekend. We're so lucky to be able to make the most of it".

Rob was a dab hand at making the most of everything. His catch phrase was "treat yourself." This treating ensured that he was constantly enjoying experiences that made him feel good. It might be something as simple as going into a luxurious hotel for a cup of coffee, or buying a plant or a CD that he loved, or taking the time to go for a drive or a walk in a beautiful place; all little treats, but ones which gave him enjoyment. If it is true that when we pass over we judge ourselves on whether we have made the most of every opportunity to take pleasure in life, Rob will pass with flying colours. He, more than anyone I knew, savoured even the simplest of things. It only occurred to me then that his way of dealing with life was not far removed from the one which Tara was advocating. He was constantly doing things which made him smile and feel happy. No matter what the world threw at Rob his philosophy was; "This too will pass."

"I have your boots in the car," he said bounding up the steps of the hotel. "I brought your stick as well. I know you said you might not be up to a big hike, but just in case. Oh, by the way, Joanne sends her regards. You need never worry about burglars," he smiled. "No one would get into your house without Joanne seeing them. I had only just pulled up when she was out asking about you. I told her you were doing ok and that I was coming to see you today."

Marie, at reception, gave me a conspiratorial smile when we entered the foyer, obviously thinking that Rob was my boyfriend. While I regarded him as a fun, positive presence, she was clearly seeing him in the physical, as a tall, athletic looking guy, with ruffled, unruly blonde hair, and a ready smile. Her warm greeting resulted in him introducing himself, and engaging her in a conversation which lasted for at least ten minutes, during which time he told her where he was from, what he worked at, and why he was there. Rob believes that we should communicate positively with everyone we meet and that this positive engagement helps all concerned. On this occasion it resulted in Marie treating us to a delicious packed lunch, courtesy of the hotel.

"I'm so glad to see you. I've been worried about you," he said when we sat down at the window looking out on the strand. "I loved Lucy too," he continued, stating the obvious, "and I miss her every day. When I'm working in the garden I think of her. She never lost her sense of wonder. Every time a flower blossomed she got excited. She said it was waking up. Maybe now it's her time to waken up. Maybe it's now Lucy's time to blossom."

"What do you mean Rob?"

"Well when she was here she was very frail. There were so many things that she couldn't do. She couldn't come hiking with us. She never came dancing either, or learned to swim, or drive, or had a boyfriend, or went shopping with friends for girly things, or wore makeup, or even enjoyed an ice cream, or a bar of chocolate, or a fizzy drink without feeling sick afterwards. Maybe her time has come to enjoy an existence without pain. Maybe she is now soaring completely free, unfettered by her impediments. That's how I like to imagine her. That's what consoles me," he said as the tears rolled down his face.

That thought had never occurred to me before. I had been too preoccupied with my grief and sense of loss to consider her passing from Lucy's perspective. Perhaps Rob was right. Perhaps she was now happier than she had been here, where she was constantly struggling to overcome the many challenges which she had faced. That thought gave me great consolation. It was a consideration which I was going to hold on to in the future.

"There's a time to refrain from mourning Rachael," he said as we sat into the car. "We are alive. We are free to enjoy all the wonders of the world. So let's give thanks and be grateful."

"Keep the thoughts positive," Tara had said. It was hard to do otherwise when Rob was around.

"Where to?" he asked.

"Didn't you say something about a trek in the Hiker's World?"

"Yes, it's on page 21."

I opened the magazine and started to read.

The Wicklow Way is a long-distance moderately difficult hike which extends over the counties of Dublin, Wicklow, and Carlow, on Ireland's east coast. In common with all the other long-distance walking routes in Ireland it passes through areas of exquisite natural beauty. But that is not its only appeal. Along this 132 km. (82 mile) route the hiker encounters both the highest pub in Ireland, and one of the smallest, the waterfall which nearly drowned a King, the grave of a brave Irish Prince; the burial place of a Saint; an estate of the famous Guinness family; the valley where history is written in stone; and all this against the backdrop of stunning scenery and in splendid isolation within a short distance of Dublin city. Meeting six people on the hills, even in the height of the summer season, would be considered a crowd. When recounting your adventures in a cosy pub in Clonegal, at the end of this memorable hike, superlatives will be the order of the day."

"What do you think?" Rob asked.

"Lead the way," I replied without hesitation. "It sounds amazing."

The official starting point of the Wicklow Way is in Marlay Park, a 121 hectares (300 acres) suburban recreational park about nine kilometres (5.5 miles) from Dublin city centre. It comprises woodlands, ponds and walks, a nine hole par three golf course, football and cricket pitches, tennis courts, and children's playgrounds. As Rob drove out of the car park and followed the way mark up the steep hill we both looked at one another and laughed. No words were necessary. We each knew that the other was recalling an incident which had happened a few years previously while we were hiking on the Pennine Way, the long-distance trek along the mountain range which forms the backbone of England. Starting in Edale in Yorkshire, it takes the hiker through the Dales National Park, along the Pennine Mountains, and over the Cheviot hills into Scotland. A free drink in The Border Hotel in Kirk Yeltholm marks the end of the walk which started 434 kilometres, (270 miles) and nearly three weeks away. The beauty of the trek is that it passes through some of the most remote countryside in Britain, making it possible to walk for many miles without any trace of human habitation. One of the downsides of this however, is that some of the stages require hikes of over 32 kilometres, (20 miles) to reach accommodation for the night. Walking these distances over rough, undulating terrain can be quite hard going. It's even tougher when you're carrying all your gear in your rucksack, as we were.

It was only the second day of the hike. The climb ahead looked pretty vicious. I'd been struggling for some time, but was too proud to acknowledge it. Now I had to come clean.

"I can't go on," I admitted to Rob. "The rucksack is killing me."

"Me too," he replied. "We'll have to get rid of some stuff."

When we collapsed down on the hill and opened the bulging backpacks all manner of things exploded onto the ground: water, fruit and sandwiches for lunch; clothes to walk in; clothes to go sightseeing in; clothes to party in; and clothes just in case; clothes, clothes, clothes; far too many clothes; shoes to ramble in, shoes to dance in, shoes for comfort, shoes, shoes, shoes.

"They'll have to go," Rob said, looking at his pile of gear, "and so will the booze," he added with regret.

On the way through Dublin Airport we had made contingency plans for the times when we would be too tired, or too late, to go to the pub for a nightcap. Rob had bought a litre bottle of Irish whiskey, and I one of Bailey's liqueur. We reckoned a combination of both would produce a cocktail with a kick. But the glass filled bottles weighed a ton. They'd have to go. We had to lighten our loads. As we couldn't possibly consider wasting the precious liquid we sat down and started to drink the delicious mix. Under normal circumstances we'd have had no problem consuming quite a weight of the fluid, but we had to be moderate.

There were still many miles to go before journey's end. We were in a quandary. What were we to do?

Help arrived in the form of Steve, out walking his dog. He gladly accepted our invitation to join us for a drink. And, proving that three heads are indeed better than two, he helped resolve our problem. "Pour the drink from the two bottles into one," he advised when we had made good inroads into both, "And give me the empty. I'll drop it into my local."

Problem solved!

It was surreal. Two hikers on a hillside in Yorkshire, drinking cocktails fit for a King, with a complete stranger at 10 a. m. The funniest thing was that Steve was drinking his from a collapsible metal mug, embellished with the Irish flag, which Rob had brought as a back up in case the plastic cap of his flask got broken.

"Do you know something," he observed philosophically as we prepared to journey on, "possessions only weigh you down." I wasn't sure whether his big smile was as a result of this thoughtful observation, or due to the lovely warm glow which I was also feeling. I suspect it was the latter.

I could only imagine the views which were visible from the Three Rock Mountain high above us, as we drove along the road trying to stay as close as possible to the Wicklow Way.

Following a route by car can in no way capture the essence of a hike. That wonderful feeling of being in the now can only be experienced when all the senses of sight, hearing, smell, touch, and taste are totally immersed in nature. However the car does have its advantages; we reached Johnnie Fox's Pub in a matter of minutes, feeling and looking fresh, rather than exhausted and bedraggled after a few hours hiking. This, the highest pub in Ireland, is renowned for its food and its music. The décor was amazing. Old bed pans, irons, hot water bottles, farm implements, and items of clothing decorated the walls and ceilings.

"That's the highest pub off the list," I remarked to Rob when we got back to the car. "I wonder what comes next."

Within a short space of time we were in Crone Wood looking at the waterfall which nearly drowned a King. This falls, the highest in Ireland, is situated in the grounds of the Powerscourt estate in Enniskerry, Co. Wicklow. On this beautiful calm day, observing the gentle flow of the water, it was hard to believe that it nearly took the life of the King of England, and the then Lord Powerscourt. During George 1V's visit to Ireland in 1821, he travelled to Enniskerry to visit his loyal subject, Lord Powerscourt. Greatly honoured by his Majesty's visit, Lord Powerscourt pulled out all the stops. Everything possible was done to ensure that the estate was seen in all its glory. The beautiful gardens were manicured. The Dargle River was dammed above the falls, and a special viewing platform erected from which the King could enjoy the spectacle of the released waters cascading down. However George delayed too long at the wonderful lunch prepared in his honour and had to leave without seeing the waterfall. Lord Powerscourt was very disappointed that his Majesty had missed the spectacle which he had arranged for him. His disappointment quickly turned to relief however when the waters were released. The desired effect was achieved. The water powered down with mighty force and washed away the viewing platform at its base. Both Powerscourt and King George had had a lucky escape.

Looking eastwards, we could see all across the sweep of Dublin Bay from Wicklow Head to the south, past Howth on its northern edge, and way beyond to the Mourne Mountains in County Down. The city of Dublin with its one million plus inhabitants was also clearly visible, but here on the mountain we were alone. It was as if we were the only people on the planet.

"I don't think we'll find a restaurant with a better view than this," Rob said sitting down on a grassy hillock and taking our sandwiches out of his rucksack.

Seated up there above the world, with the sun shining down, in the company of a good friend, I made an effort to tune into the happy vibration which I felt and brought it consciously into my body as Tara had suggested.

"Are you asleep?" Rob asked after a few minutes. It was not unknown for one or the other of us to nod off in similar circumstances in the past.

"No, I'm just working on my appetite," I replied sitting up and removing the wrapping from my sandwich.

"Ah! This is the life," Rob said as he did every time we sat down to eat in the great outdoors.

"I wouldn't call the Queen my aunt," we added in unison and laughed, meaning every word.

A few miles further along the way the Guinness estate nestled in the safety of the valley between Djouce Mountain on the one side, and Fancy on the other. Deer grazed on the lawn which was lapped by the waters of Lough Tay. The recent heavy rain had muddied the Cloghoge River as it flowed through the bog lands. This in turn had coloured the lake. Its deep brown water, edged with golden sand, was reminiscent of a pint of Guinness. Perhaps that was why Ernest Guinness had purchased the 5,000 acre estate as a wedding present for his youngest daughter Oonagh in 1937, when she married Lord Oranmore and Browne. It is presently the home of their son Garech Browne (De Brún), a supporter of the arts.

I knew where our next stop would be. On the road between Luggala and Glendalough I informed Rob of the legend of Saint Kevin's tomb. An hour later he rejoined me on the seat where I was beaming a healing smile, inspired by the beauty of the place, to my inner organs. I didn't have to ask. His grin said it all.

Before we left Glendalough Rob checked the map. "We'll have to make a small detour to get to the Prince's last resting place," he said having studied it in silence for a few moments.

I had to smile thinking how far we'd advanced from the days when we determined the route by following the imprint of other people's boots. Unfortunately, we sometimes neglected to ask if the people wearing those boots were going where we wanted to go. Of course Tracker always found the way, eventually!

However he was now not only an instinctive guide, but a scientific one as well, courtesy of the mountain skills course which I had given him for Christmas. With his natural homing devise, and his map and compass expertise, he was a formidable force. Twenty minutes later, we stood in a tiny cave deep in the wilds of Wicklow and read the following inscription from a simple granite stone:

"Insan áit seo, de réir bhéaloideas
na ndaoine de cailleadh
Árt Ó Néill
Le linn dó féin agus
Aodh Rua Ó Dómhnail bheith ar an
Slighe ó Caisleán Átha Cliath go
Gleann Maolugra sa bhliadhain 1592
Pro Fide et Patria."
[*In this place, according to folklore, Art O Neill died while he and Red Hugh O' Donnell were on their way from Dublin Castle to Glenmalure in 1592*]

The men referred to were heirs to the powerful O' Neill and O 'Donnell dynasties of Tyrone and Donegal. They had been kidnapped and imprisoned in Dublin Castle by English agents in the hope of forcing their rebellious fathers to swear allegiance to the British crown. On Little Christmas night, 6th January 1592, after many years in captivity they, together with Art's brother, succeeded in escaping from Dublin Castle; the only people ever to do so. Inadequately clothed and emaciated after many years in captivity, they left Dublin and headed for the home of their ally, Fiach Mac Hugh O' Byrne in Glenmalure 55 kilometres, (35miles) away.

That added to the poignancy of the story. They had almost made it. Only one more mountain stood between this cave and O' Byrne's stronghold. However Red Hugh O' Donnell did succeed in reaching Glenmalure, and from there he returned home to Donegal. On his father's death he became the leader of the O'Donnell clan and a fierce opponent of English rule in Ireland. Sadly he too died far from home. Tradition has it that he was poisoned by a traitor while in Spain, where he had gone to seek help to continue his fight against the British forces in Ireland.

On the way back to the car we sat down on the banks of the river which the Princes had more than likely used as a navigational tool. At that moment there was nowhere else I would rather have been. The extent of the world's beauty, grandeur, and abundance, was so clearly in evidence there. I could actually feel myself physically stronger and calmer than I had felt in a long time. My crown chakra was obviously being charged, as Tara had said it would, by being outdoors in creation. Then I thought of the many patients who would surely benefit greatly from exposure to the beauty, colour, and abundance of nature afforded by this, and similar places. Perhaps, I thought, the world's ills are in no small way due to the fact that we spend so much time indoors, totally removed from the earth from which we came.

I recalled the Prophet's answer when the people of Orphalese asked him to speak on houses;

"But you children of space, you restless in rest, you shall not be
trapped or tamed.
You shall not fold your wings that you may pass
Through doors, nor bend your heads that they strike not
Against a ceiling, nor fear to breathe less walls should
Crack and fall down.
You shall not dwell in tombs made by the dead for the living.
And though of magnificence and splendour, your
House shall not hold your secret nor shelter your longing.
For that which is boundless in you abides in the
Mansion of the sky whose door is the morning mist,
And whose windows are the songs and silences of night."

"I believe there's a lovely inn in Glenmalure," Rob said getting up from the river bank. "I'm more than ready for a nice lunch."

"Oh yes, Glenmalure is that alright!" the barman agreed. "It's remote and wild and beautiful. But it's also treacherous. You could have a lovely morning here in the valley but a deadly, life threatening afternoon on the mountains. The cloud can roll in without warning, and with the sheer cliffs, and heather covered terrain, it's an extremely dangerous place, unless you know it well. That's why historically it was the most notorious area of rebellion in Wicklow."

After our lunch we investigated the wall coverings which recounted the rich history of the area in pictures, poetry, and newspaper cuttings. There was even a plan of Fiach Mac Hugh O Byrne's stronghold at Ballincor, which the bar man said was down the road in the direction of Rathdrum.

The story of Michael Dwyer, another great Wicklow rebel leader, was also told there. Like Fiach Mac Hugh, he too had used his knowledge of the mountains to conduct a guerrilla type offensive against the British forces long after the 1798 rebellion had been quashed in other parts of the country. In an effort to subdue him, in 1800, the English King was forced to commission the building of the 69 kilometre, (43 mile) long Military Road, to make the hills more accessible to his soldiers and their weapons. When finally captured Michael Dwyer was exiled to Australia. A picture of the impressive monument which marks his tomb hangs on the wall of the inn.

"These hills produced great heroes," the barman observed, noting our interest in the historical memorabilia. "Go up the valley," he said. "Their history is written in stone."

On a giant granite boulder on the side of the road, we read the inscription which commemorated the celebrated deeds of the O'Byrne chief, who had aided the two princes on their escape from Dublin Castle.

"An glean
In ar bhris
Fiacha Ó'Broin
[Fiach Mac Hugh O' Byrne]
Cath ar Gallaibh

1580 A.D."
[This is the glen where Fiach Mac Hugh O' Byrne waged war on the foreigner in 1580 A.D.]

Michael Dwyer's exploits were immortalised on the other side of the same boulder.

"Sa glen sea bhí
A longfort ag
Mícheál O'Duibhir
Michael Dwyer
Agus a chuid laochra
1798A.D."
[In this glen Michael Dwyer and his warriors had their headquarters in 1798.]

Further up the glen those warriors were also honoured in stone with the following words;
In remembrance of those who fought bravely
For justice and freedom from these mountains
Martin Burke   Hugh Vesty Byrne   William Casey   Arthur Devlin
James Doyle   Michael Dwyer   James Farrell   Patrick Grant
John Harmon   Joseph Holt   James Kelly   Sam Mc. Allister
Michael Malon   John Mernagh   William Young and the many more
Solas siorraí ar a namanacha dílse.[Eternal light on their loyal souls.]

The track from Glenmalure to Aughavanna was very steep, but once there we were out of the hills and coasting. On the way between the villages of Tinahely and Shillelagh we found our final quest, one of the smallest pubs in Ireland. It was called The Dying Cow.

"How did it get its name?" Rob asked the barman, looking around what was in fact the small front room of a little farm house surrounded by green fields.

Obviously well practised at recounting the tale, the barman leaned on the counter and spoke in a hushed voice. "The story goes," he began, "that years ago the owner of this establishment got the reputation, whether justly or unjustly, of keeping illegal drinking hours. Word got to the local constabulary, and they determined to catch her, reportedly a widow woman, in the act. One night they called long after closing time and the place was buzzing."

"This is a very serious matter," the sergeant said. "You'll be closed down for this. You'll lose your licence."

"But I've done nothing wrong Sergeant," the widow protested.

"Do you think I'm stupid woman? These people are all still drinking at two o' clock in the morning. How can you explain that?"

"Very simply, Sergeant. My prize cow went down in the ditch and I couldn't get her out. All my good neighbours came to give me a hand, and now I'm repaying them with a "thank you" drink. And so The Dying Cow was named."

We arrived back in Bray just after 8 p.m. When I suggested to Rob that he stay the night he responded in the affirmative, as I knew he would.

"Perfect," was his exact reply.

When he was settled in his room, I went to mine to prepare for dinner. Once again a line from one of Pádraig Mac Piarais' poems came to mind; *Giorraíonn beirt bóthar.* [Two shorten the road]. I didn't know whether it was due to the good company; or to the air that I was deep breathing at intervals throughout the day; or to the positive self talk that I was playing in my head; or to a combination of all these things, but whatever it was, I was feeling a little brighter.

After dinner we walked the promenade to the harbour. It was getting dark but there was a lot of activity around the Harbour Bar. Between it, and the low wall which separated it from the path, there were a number of tables with lighted candles. These were all occupied.

"What about a night cap?" Rob asked. "This looks like a lively spot. Is that ok with you, or are you too tired?"

"No that's fine Rob. I'd like that."

The place was packed. They were four deep at the bar. I looked around to see if there was standing room anywhere and managed to take the place of two people who were leaving. Placing my bag territorially on the narrow ledge which ran along the wall I waited while Rob got the drinks.

"I'm sorry it took so long," he apologised. "I was talking to Tara. She's over there with a group of friends," he said, nodding in the direction of the bar.

"Anyone we know?" I asked straining to have a look.

Rob smiled. "No, she introduced them to me, but there were no familiar faces there."

"Have you heard anything?" I asked. There was no need to elaborate. He knew that I was talking about romance. And I knew he was the person who'd know. Earlier, when I'd revealed to him what I considered to be my news about Tara, he'd informed me that he'd known for ages about her change of direction. In fact he knew so much more than I did. He could tell me where and what she had studied to qualify her for her new role. I was impressed.

"Sláinte," we toasted. "To good friends and the great outdoors."

Rob left after lunch on Sunday. I was lonely to see him go. The time spent in his company had been really refreshing. It had reminded me of the fun we'd had on our numerous wild escapades. It had left me feeling once again the desire to experience the joy, the freedom, and the exhilaration of walking a long-distance path. I wanted to feel the sun on my face and the wind in my hair. I had been so caught up in the fear of experiencing another panic attack that I had forgotten to appreciate the times when I was feeling fine. But it was impossible to concentrate on negative emotions when Rob was around. He was the most positive person I had ever met. And he treated, not just himself, but others too with kindness and respect. He made no demands and had no expectations. He was a one-off. I was lucky to have him in my world. I had never fully appreciated that fact before. It had taken my illness to teach me to value many things which I had taken for granted, my health, my independence and Rob.

WATER

On the third night of the course I arrived at 7.55 p.m. just ahead of Tara, who was once again looking chic in what I now considered her signature style; a simple, straight, knee length green dress, navy patent stiletto shoes, and an amber necklace which matched her drop earrings. Her hair was plaited and wrapped around her head. She looked elegant and beautiful.

My customary chair was vacant, so once again I sat facing David. He looked so much cleaner. His hair had been cut and his beard trimmed.

"Tonight we're going to talk about water," Tara said.

"Water," I thought. "What can one say about water other than that it hydrates and cleans us?" But when Tara began by reminding us that we are acquainted with water before we meet our parents, I knew that there would be a unique Tara slant on the evening.

"From the moment of conception it is the element which supports and protects our life," she said. "It is the medium which nourishes us and helps our development. By inhaling the amniotic fluid we ensure the normal development of the lungs, and swallowed amniotic fluid creates urine, and contributes to the formation of meconium. Water also acts as a shock absorber protecting us from injury while in the womb, so from our very inception it plays a hugely important role in our lives. It constitutes 92% of the blood stream through which it delivers vital supplies of oxygen and nutrients to all the cells of the body, and makes up approximately 75% of our brains, 72% of our bodies, and the same proportion of planet earth, making it by far the biggest constituent of both us and our world."

The more she spoke, the more obvious it became that she had a huge appreciation for this liquid, which she had described as the body's second most essential requirement after oxygen.

"It has many physical attributes," she said in a voice full of admiration. "In fact you could say that it embodies all possible material properties. It can be a mighty force, or a gentle stream, it can be hot, or cold, liquid, solid, or vapour. It can flow, or freeze. It can support life, or extinguish it. It is an ally. It can be an enemy. It cleans and heats our homes, cooks our food, facilitates life in the rivers and oceans, powers generators and mills, extinguishes fire, and provides pleasure for skaters, sailors, and fishermen."

"That sounded like an ode to water," Mike commented when she paused for breath.

Tara smiled. "I certainly have enormous respect for it; a respect which I must admit has greatly increased since I have come to live in Bray. The many changing faces of the sea and the river fascinate me. One moment the water can be calm and smooth as glass. In a few hours it can be crashing over the harbour wall threatening lives and homes. It's like magic."

"I agree," Mike said. "You're right. It is magic."

"But of course it is only natural that it would resonate with us," she continued, "since, as I have said, it is our first experience of planet earth, and it constitutes a whopping 72% of us and of our world."

"72%!" Carol mused incredulously. "That's nearly three quarters of us. I didn't realise that," she added shaking her head.

"Yes," Tara said. "Its importance to our lives is demonstrated by the fact that we can only survive for three or four days without it. Obviously, since it comprises such a large part of us, it is essential that the water we give our bodies is pure and life-supporting. And tonight we are going to explore how we can ensure that. Tonight we will learn how to harness water's ability to carry vibrations to provide us with positive energy," she said reaching into her bag and taking out the notes for the session.

"As is clear from pictures of drought ridden countries all living things need water. Without it there is no growth and people die," she said handing the papers to Liz who proceeded to pass them around. "The brain, the body's driving force, must be properly hydrated for the body to work well. Dehydration can result in fuzzy thinking, lethargy, and errors in times of decision making," she continued, looking around to see if everybody had received a copy of her notes. "Since every thought is an electrical impulse, and so requires water, it is imperative that we are always well hydrated. If not, the body, in an effort to preserve the life of the brain, will take water from the other organs. This can obviously have a major detrimental effect on the other body parts, most especially on the heart, our second most important organ, and the one with the second biggest water requirement. It can result in strokes, heart attacks, high cholesterol, constipation, and many other illnesses," she said quite emphatically.

Then, as if for the doubters among us, she added that there was ample medical evidence to support water's importance to preserve health, to boost physical performance, to aid kidney function, to improve digestion, to maintain cognitive ability and memory, to help maintain the correct pH balance, and to prevent cavities in teeth.

"You'll find research to substantiate what I have said in tonight's handout," she said with the air of someone who wanted to move on to something else, something more exciting.

"How much water do you recommend to drink in a day?" Mike asked.

"From what I've read best practise suggests that we replenish the two litres which we lose through sweating and breathing. However this can vary from individual to individual; for example if one is engaged in physical activity, or exercise which causes the body to lose moisture through perspiring, then more may well be necessary."

She also added that, since alcohol has a dehydrating effect on the body, it was advisable to have a glass of water with each alcoholic drink to avoid a hangover, which is the brain's reaction to moisture loss, and that since many of us wake up dehydrated it was advisable to start the day with a glass of water. "Since the water we drink circulates into every organ, muscle, cell, artery, vein and capillary it is essential that it is as positively charged as possible," she said pausing for a moment as she looked around the group. "And now I would like to make you aware of fascinating research findings which enable us to do just that. By acting on this information the results, as Mike said, may indeed prove magical."

Then holding up a slim, hard covered book, she asked us to accept with an open mind what she was about to say, informing us that the book contained photographic evidence of the research findings of Dr. Masaru Emoto, a Japanese scientist. She described his research, the result of twenty years work, as amazing. Before she advised us of this research she outlined how Dr. Emoto's fascination with water had begun when, as a child, he was intrigued with its ability to change form from liquid, to solid, to vapour. His fascination was further spiked by the realisation that every one of the billions of snowflakes which fall to earth each year is distinct and unique. This inspired him to explore water's capacity to form crystals. She explained that, possibly in an effort to determine what exactly it was that made one crystal differ from another, he had taken water from different locations; from pure water sources, and from the reservoirs of many major cities, to make into crystals. He found in many cases that city water would not form even the basic hexagonal shape. Yet when he exposed it to positive vibrations, the crystals formed were as beautiful as those formed from pure water.

"What do you mean by exposing it to positive vibrations?" Carol asked.

"He found that when the water was placed within the range of beautiful music, or when positive words, or blessings and prayers were spoken over it, that it formed stunning crystals."

"That's incredible," Mike said, expressing exactly what I was thinking.

"Yes," Tara agreed, "and if that sounds amazing, even more amazingly he found that when the water was exposed to the written word it responded in the same way, seemingly absorbing the positive vibration and actualizing it to form beautiful crystals. Exposure to the written word was as effective as exposure to the spoken one. As you will see in the book," she continued, "he produced perfect crystals by exposing city water to the words; mum, dad, love, thanks, joy, abundance, and friend, proving the power of both words and water to carry the vibrations to heal or destroy. His work, as well as emphasising the amazing power of water, is also supporting another of our strategies, the absolutely critical need to affirm one's self and to keep the voice in the head positive."

"Did he recommend any words as being more effective than others?" Mike asked.

"Yes he found the words love, and thanks, produced the most spectacular crystals. But the flip side is quite disturbing. When exposed to words like; fool, ugly, stupid, and evil, the effects were devastating. The pictures of crystals portraying the effects of these words resemble shattered ice, shapeless, smashed, and ugly. Based on his research, the importance of using positive, compassionate, and gentle words, when addressing ourselves and others is obviously extremely important, because the vibrations are transmitted to our water content, which as I've said constitutes a huge part of us.

I would also like you to note the proven negative effect of overexposure to electromagnetic fields on us," she said holding the book aloft and pointing to a picture which I couldn't quite see. "As is clear from these photos, crystals formed from water left sitting in front of a computer for a number of hours, or water exposed to the field of a cell phone, or heated in a microwave oven, are distorted and ugly, and in no way resemble those formed from water charged with positive vibrations. Just take a look," she said as she handed Carol "The Miracle of Water."

Carol flicked through it stopping at the first page of photographs.

"Oh they're beautiful," she said as she studied them with a smile on her face. But, with a turn of the page, her expression changed and she became very serious. "Oh my goodness," she said handing the book to Mike as if happy to get rid of it. "I'm glad we have no television, or microwave, or cell phones, or computer. It's an ill wind," she added enigmatically. "Just look at the damage exposure to those electromagnetic fields can do. As for the effect of nasty words on people's water content!" She trailed off, as if words had failed her.

"That book had a huge impact on me," Tara said, nodding her head in agreement. "I went out immediately and bought a filter jug to ensure the purity of my drinking water. Then I printed the words love, thanks, health, abundance, happiness, on a piece of card and placed the jug on top of it beside my music centre to charge it positively. And now, before I take a drink, I thank God for the water, and ask Him to bless it with His love, light, and healing."

"What do you think Mike?" she asked as he passed on the book to Sean.

"I'm amazed," he said. "It's truly hard to believe, but I have read the author's qualifications and have to accept that his findings are scientifically endorsed."

I noticed that Sean just gave the book a cursory glance before passing it on.

While the reaction of the others had indicated the impact of the photos, I was still totally unprepared for what I saw. The pictures of the crystals formed by exposure to the words; love, gratitude, peace, exhilaration, happiness, friendship, Mum, Dad, resembled a shower of snowflakes, each different but beautiful. Equally disturbing, as Tara had indicated, was the proven negative effect on crystals formed from water which had been exposed to electromagnetic fields and nasty words. They looked exactly as she had suggested, as if a piece of ice had been thrown onto the ground and had shattered. There was also a dramatic difference in the crystals formed in response to the words convenience foods, and home cooking. The water exposed to the former words didn't even form the basic shape, while the water charged with the positive vibration of home cooking, created a beautifully incandescent crystal, surrounded by six identical miniature angelic forms positioned at evenly spaced corners.

Since I was the last person to receive the book I didn't feel rushed to pass it on, and so I turned to the back cover to read the author's qualifications. Dr. Masaru Emoto was described as an internationally renowned researcher, lecturer, and best-selling author. He was a graduate of Yokohama Municipal University, a Dr. of Alternative Medicine and President Emeritus of The International Water for Life Foundation.

Tara concluded that we were to be mindful that water forms the biggest part of us, and that its ability to carry vibrations makes it a very powerful ally in maintaining health. She urged us to use this knowledge to our advantage by exposing our drinking water to positive vibrations; to the rays of the sun, to beautiful music, and by speaking positive words of appreciation, thanks, and blessings over it. She stressed again and again that it was our responsibility, for the sake of our health and happiness, to ensure that all the vibrations which it came in contact with were positive and life enhancing.

"On that point of happiness," she added. "Dr. Emoto found a correlation between the amount of water in the body, and the person's happiness level. A well hydrated body is happier. That's another very valid reason for making sure that the body is adequately hydrated. In the words of Robert Louis Stevenson;

"The man is a success who has lived well, laughed often and loved much."

"Any questions or observations?" she asked as she usually did at the end of each session.

"I'm going to do exactly as you do," Carol said. I'm going to expose the water I drink to positive vibrations. It doesn't require any effort and it's worth a try."

I nodded in agreement.

"Once our bodies are properly oxygenated and hydrated the next most important requirement is good nourishment," Tara continued. "There is a wealth of information available about food, and many many fad diets which go in and out of fashion, but on this sheet I have outlined points of nutrition which are constant, and which have the health of the body as their main priority."

The sheet which she passed around was clearly laid out and the information was succinct.

There are three food groups, she had typed; carbohydrates, proteins and fats. A healthy balanced diet supplies a sufficiency of each.

Carbohydrates are found mainly in grains, vegetables, fruit, legumes, and dairy products. To ensure the proper functioning of the brain, heart, and body, carbohydrates should constitute 50% of our calorie intake. During digestion they are converted into glucose which the blood stream then carries to those parts of the body which use energy, like the brain, which can use 75% of the total bodily intake, the heart, and the muscles.

As well as supplying the body with glucose, which energises it, carbohydrates are rich in essential nutrients; fibre, vitamins, minerals, and antioxidants, all of which play a vital role in protecting us from serious illnesses such as heart disease, cancer and stroke.

Protein: The best sources of protein are; low-fat meats, skinless poultry, seafood, low-fat dairy foods, eggs, soy, and beans. Our muscles, organs, skin and hair, in fact about 16% of our body weight is made up of protein. It is an essential part of any healthy diet as it rebuilds and repairs muscle and organ damage. It also plays an important part in the digestive process by slowing it down, and thus controlling blood sugar levels, keeping us feeling full, alert and satisfied.

Fats: There are 4 types of fats. The good fats are mostly vegetable-based oils. The best are those that are highest in monounsaturated fats, such as olive and rapeseed oil. These oils have a beneficial effect on cholesterol levels and are good for the heart. Olive oil is used extensively in the Mediterranean countries where the population traditionally has a low rate of heart disease. Include fats containing Omega-3 in the diet. This protects the heart and is essential for brain function.

Eat three meals and three snacks a day. Breakfast should consist of a slow release carbohydrate, which is low in protein, and fat. This makes porridge, or any whole grain, a good choice. For a balanced meal at lunch and dinner imagine the plate divided into four quarters. Half the plate should contain vegetables, with a quarter each of carbohydrate and protein. Snacks can consist of I piece of fruit, or a handful of cherries or grapes, or a low fat yogurt, or 3 plain biscuits. To ensure the body has a constant supply of glucose don't skip any meals or snacks.

At the bottom of the page she had added in emphasis; how we eat is as important as what we eat. Our saliva is particular to each of us. It is as distinctive as our D.N.A. and contains the unique digestive enzymes which our body needs. For effective absorption, chew your food thoroughly, saturating it with saliva. This will greatly aid digestion.

When we had had sufficient time to read the page Tara emphasised that, just as with the other body essentials, it is important for optimum performance to replenish the body's glucose levels by eating slow release foods at regular intervals throughout the day. This was particularly important for those whose work involved a lot of brain activity she stressed.

"What are slow release foods?" Carol asked.

"These are carbohydrate foods which are digested slowly, and which release their energy gradually into the blood stream thus supporting the body with a steady supply of power. You may have noticed a GI label on various foods in the supermarket. This stands for Glycemic Index, which is a medical system for measuring the speed at which the digestive system breaks down various foods into glucose, the body's source of energy. The lower the GI index, the slower the release of energy, and the better the body feels because the energy is released by degrees and so the organs are kept happy with a steady supply of fuel. On the other hand high GI foods, usually highly processed and sugary foods, release their glucose quickly. This results in the body feeling hungry soon afterwards and craving more glucose, which is then stored as fat. If this cycle continues, obesity can result," she warned.

As with all the other strategies she stressed the importance of balance. "A little bit of everything. We are meant to enjoy the abundance of the earth," she said, "and to give thanks for it." "The exception is sugar," she paused for effect, as if expecting that this statement would not be well received.

When she spoke again her words ensured that we gave her our full attention. "There are numerous studies which show that sugar not only leads to diabetes and obesity, but can also cause cancer," she said. "But three words from the research of Dr. Patrick Quillin PhD, RD, CNS, sum up the collective findings of all these studies; "Sugar feeds cancer." She articulated the words slowly, and then repeated them. "Sugar feeds cancer. These are the words of an internationally respected consultant, professor, lecturer and author, who from 1990-2000 served as the Vice President of Nutrition for a national network of American cancer hospitals. The very obvious recommendation in the light of these findings must be to avoid simple sugars," she said looking around at the group.

"Besides their proven cancer risk, foods rich in simple sugars are devoid of any nutritional value," she continued. "They are simply empty calories which fail to satisfy the body's need for sustenance, and so the body craves more and more of them, resulting in obesity. Best practise seems to suggest that a diet rich in foods as near to their natural state as possible is the one most likely to support health."

Because food also absorbs vibrations she recommended the age-old practise of all cultures and generations, of blessing our meal before eating it, and of giving thanks afterwards. She also recommended eating in a relaxed environment, preferably in the company of those we loved, from a table decorated with flowers and candles, while listening to beautiful music. "Your food will absorb these positive vibrations, and nourish you with them," she assured us.

Even when dining alone she advised pulling out all the stops, as if entertaining a loved one.

"In case it escaped you I'd like you to look at the crystal formed when the words convenience foods were taped to the water container," she said passing around the book again. "Contrast it with the one formed when the water was exposed to the words home cooking," she suggested.

I had already noted that.

Then reminding us to prepare our food with love, and to bless it before eating, and to give thanks afterwards, she brought the class to a close.

As I left the room I fell into step with Mike and Carol. Sean caught up with us in the hall as we all fastened our jackets against the rain.

"If anyone would like a lift to The Tea Cup you're very welcome to come with me," I said still feeling a little awkward about the episode at the harbour. Mike and Carol accepted my offer immediately. Sean said that he wasn't going to The Tea Cup. That he was going home. As I drove out of the car park he was heading in the opposite direction to the town.

"Normally I'd be moaning about the rain," I said turning the wipers to high speed, "but from now on I'll be blessing it. Who'd have thought that water was so powerful and interesting?" I continued, adding that because I was from the midlands it possibly hadn't played as big a part in my life as I was sure it had in theirs.

"Yeah," Mike said. "We love the sea. I don't think we could be happy living away from it. It has always been very important to us. In fact it brought us together."

"Don't bore the girl with that Mike," Carol said leaning forward from the back seat.

"No, please," I protested. "I love to hear how people met."

"We've been practically inseparable since we were kids," Mike said seeming quite happy to share this with me. "Since I was nine and Carol was five to be exact. That's the age we were when we met at a beginner's sailing class. From then on we've been best friends. We both took to the water like ducks," he laughed. "We both loved the sea; we loved to swim, sail, surf, ski, and fish, anything that involved water. So nobody was the least bit surprised when we announced that we were getting married. Our parents would have preferred if we had waited until Carol was at least twenty, but there was no stopping us. We were young and invincible," he said laughingly. "We were going to conquer the world. We planned to sail away stopping off in any port that appealed to us, working as swimming or sailing instructors, or as deck hands. We were willing to do anything to enable us to live our dream. However Kate's birth caused a postponement of our plans, as did Amy's the following year. When Cathal arrived on the scene we stopped planning. Carol became the home-maker and I went to college, studied electrical engineering, and eventually set up my own business. But no matter how busy we were we always kept up our contact with the sea. We never gave up on our dream. When times were good and there was plenty of work we saved to fund it when we retire. Now we're so thankful that we did."

"So you're going to spend your retirement sailing around the world. Lucky things," I said all bright and breezy.

For a moment Mike's happy-go-lucky façade slipped.

"Sometimes things don't go according to plan," he said as we entered The Tea Cup.

He spoke the words rather sadly, and I hoped to catch up with him inside to see what he meant by them, but we got separated and when I had had my tea I left and went back to the hotel where I read the course notes.

Under the heading water vitality Tara had listed the following studies and on the back of the page she had summarised the evening's class as follows:

Scientific evidence of the importance of water for good health:

The importance of good hydration for the prevention of chronic diseases;
Manz F. Wentz. A. Nutr Rev. 2005:52-55 [Pub Med]
Positive effects of maintenance of good hydration are shown for constipation, exercise asthma, urinary tract infections, hypertension, fatal coronary heart disease, venous thromboembolism, and bronchopulmonary disorders.

The importance of water for cognitive performance;
Dehydration by as little as 2.8% showed impaired performance on tasks examining visual perception, short term memory, and psychomotor ability. Cian C., Koulmann PA, Barraud PA, Raphael C., Jimenez C., Melin B. Psychophysiol 2000;14: 29-36.

The effects of water on kidney and cardiovascular function;
Recent studies of animals and humans suggest that a higher water intake may benefit kidney and cardiovascular function. Sontrop et al. American Journal of Nephrology 2013 37:434-442 April 17th 2013

The following studies have proved the negative effects of simple sugars on health:
-        *Warburg O. On the origin of cancer cells. Science 1956 Feb.*
-        *Digirolamo M. Diet and cancer markers. Prevention and treatment. New York Plenum Press 1994.*
-        *Moerman CJ et. Al. Dietary sugar intake in the aetiology of biliary tract cancer. Apr. 1983*
-        *Seeley S. Diet and breast cancer: the possible connection with sugar consumption.*
-        *Patrick Quillin, PHD,RD,CNS, Cancer's Sweet Tooth Nutritional Science News Apr. 2000.*

Further Reading Suggestion: News Release from Harvard Medical School titled; "Attacking Cancer's Sweet Tooth is Effective Strategy against Tumours".

Positively charged water is essential for good health.

The average adult requires about two litres of water a day.

Avoid electro magnetic fields.

Avoid all simple sugars.

Eat three meals and three snacks to maintain blood sugar levels.

Eat colourful, home cooked, food.

Bless and give thanks always.

COLOUR AND PERFUME

Early on Tuesday morning I made a 'phone call which I had been think-ing of making for the past few days; since Rob's visit in fact. Seeing him had made me realise that I missed my family, my friends, and my home. I wasn't sure whether the course had benefited me or not. Sometimes I felt a little brighter, then out of the blue panic would again threaten. However I felt my time in Bray had been of some benefit to me. Dis-tance had lent a degree of clarity to my situation. I realised that the reason why my parents didn't show their love for me as much as they had done for Lucy was because I had blocked them. I had always played the role of Miss Independent. When I'd failed to get the job in Dublin which I had set my heart on, when Peter and I had broken up and I was practically demented trying to organise the finance to keep the house, when Lucy had passed, I'd continued on relentlessly, refusing all their offers of help and support. I had created my own monster. I resolved to address that as soon as I got home. I was also looking forward to getting back to my own house and I felt that I needed to return to work. I couldn't hide away forever. I was, however, determined to continue with the course because I knew with absolute certainty that it had worked wonders for Tara. No matter how often I saw her I was still amazed at the transformation in her from that day in the surgery. So I determined to travel to Bray every Tuesday evening. It would only take a few hours and could well prove worth it.

"Rachael, it's good to hear from you. How are you?" Dr. Steven's voice boomed over the 'phone.

"I'm fine thanks Dr. Steven. I wanted to let you know that I will be returning to work on Thursday."

"That's wonderful Rachael. I'll just make a note of that."

I could hear the drawer of his desk opening, followed by the rustle of pages turning. "Let me just confirm the date Rachael, Thursday the twenty fourth."

"That's correct, Thursday the twenty fourth."

"Looking forward to having you back," he said and hung up.

That evening I was once again the first person in room two of the community centre. But this time I wasn't filled with dread. I felt that Tara's calm and capable handling of the course and the scientific evidence which she had provided in the notes was more than enough to ensure a good attendance.

David arrived, gave me his customary nod, and sat opposite me as usual. He looked very well in a maroon, fine wool sweater. The collar of a pristine white shirt was visible inside its neckline. He had also paid a visit to the barber. His normally unruly hair was neat and tidy and he was clean shaven. He looked like any normal man in his late fifties or early sixties, and was totally unrecognisable from the person who had sat across from me on the first night of the course. When he caught me looking at him he nodded. Minus the beard and mop of hair his face was now visible, as was the twinkle in his eye when he smiled. It was hard to believe that initially I had wanted to avoid him at all costs. "The difference a little care and attention makes, not only to the person themselves, but to the reaction of others to them," I thought as the door opened admitting Carol and Mike.

Rose and Tara arrived together. They were a study in contrasts. Rose, dressed in a grey top and dark pants, appeared smaller and slimmer than ever. Her face was gaunt and stressed, and the dark circles under her eyes could have been etched there in black ink. Tara stood tall and erect. Her hair was piled loosely on top of her head with curly tendrils hanging down. She wore a sky blue, sheath dress, with a light blue fabric rose pinned at the waist. Cobalt blue, Murano glass earrings matched the beads around her neck. Her neat, soft fabric bag and high heeled sandals were orange, and of course she wore a smile. As usual, in addition to being a treat for the eyes, her presence seemed to change the atmosphere in the room. There was a calmness about her. It was actually more than a calmness. There was a peace about her. I found myself thinking how wonderful it must be to have that tranquillity in the face of whatever life throws at you. Could that quality be learned, or had she always been blessed with it? I wondered. Then, by way of answer, the demented face which she had presented with in the surgery came to mind, and I knew that there was a time when she too was seriously lacking in this most desirable quality.

At eight o' clock there was a gaping hole in the circle. Sean's seat was empty. I wasn't too surprised. Sean of all of us seemed to be the least impressed with the course. I sometimes wondered why he came at all.

At a few minutes past eight the door opened and a woman, a little older than me, came in.

"I'm Sandra, Sean's wife," she said. "He's not feeling very well. Is it ok if I take his place?"

"Certainly, you're very welcome Sandra," Tara said indicating the empty chair. When Sandra had settled herself Tara began that evening's session.

"Tonight we're going to tap into another very simple strategy to energise us;" she smiled. "We're going to explore the power of light vibrations and the magic of colour."

Rose leaned forward slightly.

"As you can read later," she said holding up the customary stapled pages on which she always supplied course information, "There is ample scientific proof to suggest that if we are deprived of light we suffer illness. The most obvious consequence of this lack of light is the Seasonal Affective Disorder Syndrome, or S.A.D. This happens when the reduced amount of light in winter causes the pineal gland to produce too much of the hormone melatonin. This results in depression, over sleeping, weight fluctuations, tiredness, and sadness because the vitamin D contained in sunlight is essential for the absorption of calcium which calms the central nervous system. Because of the interconnectivity of the glandular system this lack of light impacts not only on the pineal gland, but on the entire glandular system and results in emotional imbalance, depression, lack of energy, and nervousness."

She stopped there for a moment giving us the time to absorb what she had said.

"Is there a natural cure for the sleeplessness, depression and weight loss?" Rose asked quite uncharacteristically.

This was actually the first time since the course started that she had asked a question. I was aware of this because each week she sat practically straight across from me, on the chair beside David. While her body language always indicated an interest in the topic being discussed this was the first time she had expressed that interest verbally. Observing her now, as her concentrated on Tara while waiting for an answer, she looked as petite and vulnerable as my ten year old niece. Perhaps insomnia is the cause of the black circles under her eyes, I found myself thinking, and maybe she's losing weight because of depression. That would tie in with my diagnosis of the first night; that Rose had a broken heart.

"Yes Rose," Tara replied gently, "for centuries practitioners of energy medicine have recommended exposure to daylight as a cure for the conditions you have mentioned. And now science also endorses this. Currently the conventional treatment for S.A.D. consists of exposure to bright lights for several hours each day to inhibit melatonin production."

"How can that help?" Rose asked again.

Tara explained the rationale behind the treatment by reminding us that we are powered by the vibrations of our seven chakras which access energy from the universe. She explained that each of them is tuned into the frequency of a colour.

"There are seven chakras and seven colours in natural light," she informed us. "And when working effectively, each chakra vibrates at the frequency of its corresponding colour. Exposure to the correct colour encourages the chakra to open, to pulsate, and to access energy from the universe."

It all sounded so easy, so natural and so awesome. I felt like running outside and exposing myself to the magic of the daylight which at 9.30 p.m. on that summer's evening was still available.

"How did they come to the conclusion that colour could power the body?" Rose asked.

For an instant I felt like answering that question by pointing to Tara. Her vibrantly coloured ensemble would energise anyone, just by looking at it.

In reply Tara informed us that in 1939 a Russian electrical engineer, Semyon Kirlian developed a system of photography capable of capturing the aura. This, she said, endorsed what healers and seers had known for centuries; that the body is indeed surrounded by an orb of light which contains all the colours of the spectrum.

"How did they decide which colour charged which chakra?" Rose asked again.

"It's to do with the law of resonance," Tara answered. "This is a law in physics which states that things on the same wavelength respond to, and influence, one another. By comparing the function of the chakra with the properties of the colour it is easy to match them. For example, by referencing this law, we can identify red as the colour which resonates with the base chakra. Red is the colour of blood, and this red chakra helps control our blood pressure, our activities and energy," she said.

Just as that chakra encourages action through the manufacture of adrenaline, the get up and go hormone, so she suggested that red is a vital, dynamic and energising colour which inspires activity. By eating red foods, and wearing red clothes, we too could tap into its dynamic vibration and increase our energy levels she promised. This was the reason, she said, why fast food restaurants painted their premises red. They hoped to encourage a fast turnover by tapping into the frequency of the colour.

Referring to the second chakra, which she had at an earlier session identified as the one mainly responsible for digestion, she identified orange as its energising colour, pointing out that we drink orange juice to stimulate this area and to aid elimination.

"Orange is a sociable and fun loving colour," she said smiling.

At that moment she was a case in point. Her orange sandals were definitely fun looking, and could certainly be a conversation starter.

"Orange inspires confidence," she added, just as I was thinking that one would need confidence to wear it. But then the words of Nelson Mandela came to mind; who was I not to be confident, fabulous and gorgeous? I was a child of God. There and then I resolved that the next item of clothing which I would buy would be something in bright beautiful orange. If the benefits outlined by Tara were true it would certainly prove a good investment. According to her it resonates with our pleasure centre, charges our sexual energy, and is good for the sex glands, the spleen and bladder. It also promotes creativity in the same way as its corresponding chakra governs procreation.

"I love orange," Rose said smiling, as if the very thought of the colour had made her happy.

"Well, trust the guru within and wear it, eat it and indulge yourself in it," Tara advised. "It will help you fulfil your creativity. "

"The colour for the solar plexus is self evident," she continued. "As the name suggests it is the colour of the sun; bright, beautiful yellow."

"Of course I thought, how obvious."

"Yellow is the colour we instinctively associate with happiness," she continued as I smiled, visualizing a field of daffodils. "When this chakra is working well we are joyful." Then she added that since yellow resonates with our centre of inner knowing, our gut feeling, it is seen as the colour which can stimulate our intelligence. She identified this as the reason why classrooms are often painted in this colour.

"That brings us to the halfway point," she said identifying green as the central colour, the colour of balance; the middle colour of the spectrum. This, she said, was the reason why it resonates with the heart chakra, which is located between the base and crown chakras. Its function is also one of balance, she informed us. She identified the patience, contentment, joyfulness and fun which are the result of a healthy heart chakra as being on the same frequency as the relaxing vibrations which one feels from observing the green of the countryside.

From personal experience I knew the power of green to relax and renew. As soon as I left the confines of any town or city and went into the countryside, my heart felt lighter and happier. The sight of a green space usually elicited an involuntary deep breath, followed by a huge sigh of relief, and then a smile.

At this stage Tara was explaining that the blue of the limitless expanses of sea and sky was the colour which resonates with the throat chakra, since it powers our boundless potential, creativity, and self-expression when we are in full health. She again emphasised the importance of this chakra which governs our ability to speak out for ourselves, and for the causes we believe in.

"Since blue promotes calm it resonates with the serenity and poise which are a result of the proper functioning of the throat chakra," she said. "When in good health, this chakra impacts on the nervous system, because it regulates the amount of calcium in the blood. Calcium is the body's natural tranquiliser," she reminded us. And she suggested this as the reason why many waiting rooms and hospital wards were painted blue, as it is a cooling colour which reduces fear and dispels anger.

As Tara had been indicating the benefits of each colour I had tried to visualize the items of clothing in my wardrobe. I was shocked to realise that, besides my many white blouses, the only brightly coloured garment I had was the pink dress which I had recently bought to wear to a friend's wedding. Apart from it my wardrobe was full of grey suits, black, brown, beige, and taupe skirts and slacks. In an effort to appear professional I had gone for the traditional dark, dull, business garb, and denied myself, and more importantly my patients, another healing aid. How silly I had been! It was so obvious that being attended to by some-one wearing beautiful colours would cheer the spirit and raise the patient's vibrations. As usual it was obvious when it was pointed out.

"Indigo, the deep blue of the night sky, reverberates with the chakra in the brow," Tara said as I tuned into her again. "It is considered a mystical colour, just as the third eye is seen as supernatural. Indigo relaxes, calms, inspires, and gives rest and healing to the eyes in the same way as the chakra which it governs ensures that the correct hormones and nerve impulses are circulated in the blood to maintain health, balance and calm in the system."

Finally because the crown chakra is our centre of spirituality which links us with the Divine she identified violet as the colour which resonated with it.

"It is the colour of high ideals and enlightenment; the colour traditionally worn by royalty and Princes of the Church," she said as I recalled the bishop in his purple vestments at a recent confirmation ceremony.

She then suggested that the easiest way to ensure that the energy body was being charged was to go out in the daylight, since it contains all the colours of the spectrum in proper proportion. In that way the chakras would be charged evenly and balance would result. For anyone who didn't have the energy to go walking she suggested wrapping up warmly and sitting outside to drink in the light. She also suggested gardening as a productive way of using this time spent outdoors.

Rob immediately came to mind. He was always in the open, breathing in powerful oxygen and colour. Was that the secret of his good humour, fun, and equilibrium? I wondered. Did he have the correct work, fun balance, because his chakras were equally charged, courtesy of the vibrations his energy body was constantly exposed to?

To enable us to gain maximum benefit from every breath Tara suggested that while inhaling we should visualise red going to the base chakra, orange to the second, yellow to the third, green to the heart, blue to the throat, indigo to the mid eye and violet to the crown.

"Bring the chakra colours indoors," she suggested with her usual enthusiasm. "Scatter brightly coloured cushions all over the house, and when you feel tired wrap up in a relaxing blue or green fabric, or whatever colour appeals to you. Have fun with colour. Wear colourful clothes and vibrantly coloured scarves, jewellery, and accessories. Notice the way people will react positively to you in your beautiful attire, healing both you and them with the energy of their smile. And remember to eat at least five vividly coloured pieces of fruit and vegetables every day. Keep the colours balanced. This helps ensure that you're getting all the minerals and vitamins that you need. Colour is such a beautiful strategy," she added and at this stage she had completely convinced me.

"Has perfume any particular significance?" Rose asked.

I wondered if her question had been prompted by the fact that she had walked in with Tara and had been enveloped in the gorgeous perfume which always surrounded her. Or if it had been inspired by the previous evening's television programme which had identified Clive Christian's Imperial Majesty perfume as the most expensive perfume in the world. Made from rose oil, orris root, jasmine and Italian cinnamon it cost $215,000 for 16.9 ounces.

Whatever the reason for Rose's question Tara's answer was very interesting and informative. She identified perfume as an extremely potent aid to healing because of its influence on the hypothalamus, the body's most important gland. She informed us that as far back as 2,679 B.C. The Chinese Book of Internal Medicine detailed recipes for the application of herbs for curative purposes. That in the Trojan Bathhouse the Roman warriors massaged with perfumed oils and unguents to prepare for battle. That herbal preparations, notably frankincense were used during the Black Death to fight the plague.

She then described some of the complementary therapies which today use the odour and essence of herbs, plants and flowers to form the basis of homeopathic remedies.

She explained that aromatherapy, which is considered mainstream medicine in France, the country of its origin, uses the oils distilled from plants and herbs to effect healing. That the positive vibrations of the flowers can be absorbed in a number of ways; through the nose by adding a few drops to heated water and inhaling the fumes, by mixing it in a carrier oil such as almond, or sunflower, and by massaging it onto the skin as a perfume.

She also mentioned the Bach flower remedies. This system of healing, called after its developer, is based on transferring the pattern of the energy of the plant to the patient by collecting the dew drops from plants exposed to the rays of the early morning sun. Dr. Bach described his flower remedies as containing the essence of the plant, and as being like beautiful music or any gloriously uplifting thing. He was also quoted as saying that the dew taken from sun drenched flowers was much more potent than from those in the shade.

"All these methods incorporate the sense of smell and enable the essence of the plants to resonate with the limbic system, the body's pleasure centre, putting it in healing mode," she said addressing Rose. "Many plant essences have incredible molecular properties," she assured us. "They are antiseptic, antiviral, and insect repellent."

Then in an altogether more pensive voice she added; "I think perfume heals because it is on the God vibration."

Rose's immediate response to this statement was to smile and to nod her head in agreement as if she was having a suspicion confirmed.

"The very name perfume, from the Latin, per fume, meaning through smoke, indicates a connection with the gods," Tara continued informing us that the name had resulted from the age-old tradition of burning resins, some more precious than gold, to forge a connection between man and God.

To illustrate her point she quoted incidences from the Bible; for example in the desert of Sinai, during the Exodus from Egypt to the Promised Land, God commanded Aaron to burn sweet smelling incense every morning and every evening. His priests were also anointed with oils containing cinnamon and myrrh. On the birth of the Christ Child, together with gold, The Magi also brought gifts of frankincense and myrrh. The history books were replete with instances of its God connection, she said, and with its use and importance in all cultures and traditions. She informed us that the Egyptian's favourite perfume was called Kyphi, which means "welcome to the gods." She said that excavations carried out in the great Temple in Karnack, near Luxor, built in 4,600B.C. suggest that ante rooms were used for the preparation of scented oils and unctions with which to adorn the great god Amun. She mentioned Papyrus manuscripts from 2,700B.C. the era of King Khufu, builder of the pyramids, and a wall picture in Tutankhamen's tomb 1,324B.C., as further proof of the use of fragrant herbs, perfumed oils, and incense in ancient Egypt. Greek, Roman, Christian, Hindu and Chinese traditions all had evidence of its use in every form of worship, meditation, wedding and funeral services. She conjured up a picture of Delphi (1400B.C.), the scene of the world's most important shrine, where the Oracle priestess sat enveloped in a fragrant perfume produced by the burning of bay leaves. Holes in the floor allowed the smoke from the smouldering embers to waft upwards inducing a hypnotic state.

She also pointed to the fact that both Greek and Christian traditions believed that the sweet smell of perfume marked a visitation from the gods. Many saints are said to have died in the Odour of Sanctity. On the death of St. Theresa, The Little Flower, the perfume of roses filled the monastery where she lay. The passing of St. Theresa of Avilla, St. Faustina, and St Maximilliam of Jesus, were all apparently marked in the same way.

And on a human level she credited perfume with the beginning of the affair between Anthony and Cleopatra. She recounted how when Cleopatra, the last pharaoh, was summoned to answer questions about her loyalty to the Roman Empire, she used perfume to completely beguile Anthony. Arriving on a barge with purple sails and silver oars she reclined under a golden canopy dressed as Venus, the goddess of love. The perfume of the rose petals which covered the floor of the vessel filled the air and charmed him. He was so mesmerised by her that, rather than return to his wife and family in Rome, he accompanied her to Alexandria and spent the winter there. Thus one of the world's greatest love stories began.

At the end of the session Sandra went up to speak to Tara. I caught a snippet of the conversation as I was leaving.

"Please there's no need to apologise," Tara said as I passed. "It takes time to recover from a trauma like that."

Rose practically danced out of the room. When I sat beside her in The Tea Cup, the twinkle, which had been a mere hint on the first night when she introduced herself, was very much in evidence.

"Pretty amazing stuff, isn't it?" I said as I settled in beside her.

"Oh it's absolutely wonderful," she beamed, pouring me a cup of tea. "Of course I always knew Peter would be in the presence of beauty and light, but it's wonderful to have confirmation of it."

I didn't respond. I had no idea who she was talking about, and I didn't like to ask. She seemed about to elaborate when David joined us and the talk became more general. After a while I excused myself and went back to the hotel where I packed my bag and left it in readiness for my departure the next morning. I then read the course notes. At the bottom of the sheet Tara had summarised the evening's most important points also:

Scientific evidence of the importance of colour and perfume for good health:

The American Institute for cancer research recommends eating fruit and vegetables of rainbow colours to guard against cancer. This endorses the Institute of Colour findings which claim that light vibrations are as important to the body as vitamins and minerals. Research shows that when deprived of certain light waves we become ill.

Research carried out by Dr. John Nash Ott led him to conclude that only a full spectrum of natural light could provide full health in plants, animals and humans. Ott J. Health and Light, The Effects of Natural and Artificial Light on Man and Other Living Things, Connecticut U.S.A.

Presently there are in excess of 800 image consultancy firms in Europe. Their mission statement (claim is) that they can advise clients on how to wear colours that make them look younger, more energised, more alive, feel and look great.

Research conducted by the Institute for Colour shows that we make a judgement about a person, an environment, or product within 90 seconds of initial viewing and between 62% and 90% of that assessment is based on colour. The importance of perfume for good health

The fact that smells go straight to the hypothalamus is very significant, because this tiny organ is responsible for regulating dozens of bodily functions including temperature, thirst, hunger, blood sugar levels, growth, sleeping, waking, sexual arousal, and emotions such as anger and happiness, To smell something is to send a message to "the brain's brain," and from it to the whole body. Deepak Chopra M.D. "Perfect Health"

"Of all the senses, none surely is so mysterious as that of smell. The nature of the emanations that stir it to activity is still unknown. Its effect upon the psyche is both wide and deep, at once obvious and subtle." Dr. D. Mc. Kenzie "Study of Smells".

White light, sunlight, contains the seven colours necessary to recharge the chakras.

Spend time in the outdoors every day.

Eat brightly coloured fruits and vegetables.

Wear vibrantly coloured clothes and accessories.

Bring the rainbow colours into your home.

Wrap yourself in a relaxing blue or green cloth.

Use a perfume that you love; a fragrance that makes you feel beautiful.

HOME AGAIN

On Wednesday morning I got up, put a smile on my face, and walked tall around the room. Then before breakfast I put on my warm walking jacket and went outside to breathe. Mindful of the previous night's class I lay on the grass beside the flower bed where the sweet william, peonies, and jasmine perfumed the air. Then while inhaling I imagined the journey which the air that I was breathing had completed before reaching me. I visualised it blowing over the perfumed fields of Grasse, and the vineyards and orchards of Spain carrying with it the vibrations of the vibrantly coloured fruits and flowers growing there. As I breathed in I imagined each colour in turn powering my chakras; the red of the poppies, the orange of the nectarines, the bright yellow of the daffodils, the green of the grass, the blue of the sea, the indigo of the night sky, the purple of the violets, energising me from the base of my spine to the crown of my head.

When I had completed my six deep breaths I lay relaxed on the grass and my mind wandered. Could what Tara promised really be possible? I wondered. Could exposure to the beautiful vibrations of colour and perfume help restore me to balance and good health? By using these simple practises could I become a totally new person, energised, vital and dynamic? It seemed too good to be true. It was free, enjoyable, and I was in control. When this doubt threatened to rob me of my new found hope I did as I had become in the habit of doing and repeated a positive mantra. "Tara's strategies work," I said with deliberation.

As I sat up it seemed as if the heavens themselves were endorsing my words. There on the horizon for the entire world to see, were two beautiful, vibrant rainbows. I had never given any consideration to rainbows before. It had never occurred to me how significant they must be, heavenly bodies up there with the sun, moon, and stars in full view of all creation. Now I saw them as the encouragement I needed. There painted in vibrant abandon across the sky were the constituent

colours of the air I was breathing. There across the firmament in perfect balance were the colours which Tara said would work their magic
on us; red, orange, yellow, green, blue, indigo, and violet. An acronym
which I had learned in primary school, and which had lain buried in the
deepest recesses of my mind now came to the surface; "Ring Out Your
Great Bells In Victory. "Red, Orange Yellow, Green, Blue, Indigo and
Violet.

After breakfast I said goodbye to Marie, put my bag in the boot and
left for home. I was smiling as I pulled out of the car park, still basking
in the positive afterglow of the rainbows. I also felt empowered, knowing that I could do a lot to influence how I felt. Granted it might take
time and effort, but if feeling good was the pay off, it was worth it.
Working towards good health was my responsibility. That was a lesson
I'd have to transmit to my patients. They had responsibilities too.
Good health didn't come in a pill. The pill might help the body battle
through a hard patch, but the normal everyday rough and tumble, in
most cases, required a lifestyle change.

On the way home I drove into the shopping centre on the northern
edge of the town. Liz was outside Super Prices with three little children;
a boy of about eight, a girl who looked only slightly younger and a toddler who was strapped into the baby seat of the trolley. When I greeted
her she smiled uncertainly at me as if she couldn't place me. She
looked completely frazzled. The boy was asking if he could have a game
for his PlayStation. The little girl was pulling at her to draw her attention to the fact that her lace was open. When Liz had tied it we began
to walk into the shop together.

"Oh my bag, where's my bag?" she asked frantically looking around.

"I must have left it in the car," she said taking the keys out of her
pocket.

"Don't move from here," she warned James. "Don't run off with the
trolley or I won't let you outside the door for the next six months. Do
you hear me?"

James nodded.

"And you're not to run away either Jane. I'll be back in a minute," she said dashing out the door.

"Want a race?" James asked as soon as she'd left.

Jane nodded and they both took off squealing with delight while the child in the trolley, which James was pushing with great force, screamed in terror. I didn't know whether to follow them or to wait to tell Liz what had happened.

"They're always at that," she said when she came back clutching her bag. "I dread bringing them to the shops, or anywhere else for that matter."

We pursued the children through the supermarket. When we eventually caught up with them Liz tried to grab James but he lay down on the floor and refused to get up.

"He made me do it," Jane said as Liz waved her finger threateningly at her. James started to protest.

"I can't take any more of this," Liz said, practically in tears. "I just feel like running away. They're impossible, and that lad," she said pointing to James who was still lying on the floor, grumbling. "That lad is the boldest child in Ireland. Sometimes I feel like smacking him but he's so bold he'd ring Frank's mother and report me, and then I'd be in deep trouble."

I tried to hide a smile.

"I'm serious," Liz said almost in tears. "He has already threatened to do it and he's capable of anything."

"Well good morning," Rose said as she joined us smiling broadly and sounding very upbeat. She had arrived in the manner of Cleopatra, enveloped in perfume and looking stunning. Her azure blue dress matched her eyes and the orange scarf wrapped casually around her neck gave it a trendy look. Much as I wanted to know what had been responsible for her transformation, I didn't ask. But when I commented on how well she was looking she nodded and smiled before addressing Liz.

"You're the very person I wanted to see Liz," she said ignoring completely the antics of James who was rolling around the floor practically under her feet. "I was wondering if you knew where I could find a boy to help me with my shopping. If I could find the right child I'd give him a treat."

James stopped mumbling.

"What about this boy on the floor?" she asked as if she had only just spotted him. "Ah no, I think he's a bit too small."

James got up and stretched to his full height.

"Oh, now that I can see him properly I think he's about the right size," Rose said. "Would you like to help me?" she asked.

James nodded.

"Can I borrow him please Liz?"

"You can take them all."

"No, one is fine thank you. We'll meet you at the checkout."

"I don't know how I'm ever going to get on top of everything," Liz said cuddling the baby who was still crying. "I can't see how any amount of breathing, or telling myself how strong I am is going to help. I suppose I was just setting myself up for another disappointment thinking that Tara's course would help. She doesn't look like someone who has ever experienced stress. What do you think? Are we all naive to believe that her suggestions can work?"

I would dearly have loved to have told Liz that Tara had been through more than most people, but that was confidential information, so instead I hoped to encourage her by saying how impressive I thought the scientific evidence for each of the strategies was and how effective I found the positive affirmations.

"It's the children I should be brainwashing," she said trying to shush the baby. "Especially James. He's a right handful. He never leaves the others alone."

Then, as if on cue, we heard Rose praising James for getting the butter out of the fridge for her and for placing it so carefully in her basket. Liz shook her head.

When we got to the checkout Rose and James were already there.

"Thank you so much for helping me with the shopping James," Rose said getting down to his level and giving him her full attention.

"Now that we know one another I'll be very interested to hear from your Mammy how you're getting on."

When she told him to pick his favourite bar he choose a large bar of Dairy Milk chocolate which he held obediently in his hand. Rose had told him it had to be shared with his sisters.

Liz looked astonished.

"You're a miracle worker," she said when she had strapped the three into the car. As soon as she turned her back the wailing started.

"That's that little brat again," Liz said waving her fist threateningly at James. "Stop annoying your sister."

"I don't think I can face another day of this," she said looking distracted.

"Would it be ok with you Liz if I took James for a little while to give you a break?" Rose asked.

Liz nodded.

"James," Rose said opening the car door and putting her hand on his shoulder. "I need a boy to help me work in the garden. Since you were such a good help in the supermarket I was wondering if you'd be interested."

James nodded.

"There are a few other boys who would like the job but since I know your Mammy I'd be happy to give it to you if I could be sure that you'd behave properly. Of course I'll pay pocket money. What do you think?"

"Yeah, ok," James said smiling sweetly at Rose.

"That's settled then," she said. I'll call to your house tomorrow and if I get a good report about you, you can start work immediately."

When Liz drove off Rose went into the hairdresser and I did the fastest clothes shop I have ever done. In the space of half an hour I had visited four boutiques and had bought three dresses. By my normal standards that was exceptional. I usually spent ages trawling through racks and racks of clothes not having the slightest idea of what I was looking for. On this occasion I went into the shops and scanned the rails for red, orange, yellow, green, blue, indigo and violet. In the case of three of them I was in and out in a matter of minutes. They had nothing in the vibrant colours I was looking for. In the fourth one I was spoiled for choice. I finally decided on indigo to power my hypothalamus and to aid the proper functioning of my glandular system, and green to ensure balance. It took me a little while to choose between the red and orange. I eventually decided on the orange remembering the benefits associated with that colour, and besides I had a pink dress at home.

For just a fleeting moment I wondered if I was being very selfish buying three dresses at the same time, then at once I heard both Rob and Tara advising me that I should treat myself, and besides the dresses were medicinal. They were a tonic for my chakra system. I also bought seven lengths of fabric, one of each of the seven rainbow colours. I intended to make them into cushion covers and to scatter them around the house. If I had any left over I would wrap myself up in it when relaxing. In the book shop I purchased a copy of Dr. Emoto's book, "The Secret of Water." It is his book for children and the photos are stunning. I intended to use it to emphasise to both adult and child patients the effects which words and thoughts can have on us. Sadly the increasing instances of cyberbullying, and the tragic loss of life which resulted from it, was proof of this.

Joanne greeted me when I arrived home, declaring that I was looking a little better. It did me good to hear that. She was nothing if not candid. Had I been looking poorly she would have told me just as forthrightly.

Rob had obviously called. There was milk and a carton of soup in the fridge, and fresh bread on the counter. When I had eaten the soup and put my clothes in the washing machine, I went upstairs and opened the wardrobe. In the midst of all the blacks, greys, taupes, beiges, and browns, the pink dress which I had worn to Daisy Moore's wedding a few months previously stood out like a beacon. I took it out and hung it on the outside of the door. Tara had identified pink as the colour of universal love and the colour which a baby sees when light penetrates the womb. I also took out the red stiletto shoes which I had worn with it. They should give me a blast of energy, I reckoned. Then I went into the garden, closed my eyes, and breathed my six deep breaths. Mindful of the beautiful rainbows I directed each colour to the appropriate chakra. Then nicely relaxed I practised the inner smile before meditating for a little while.

Next morning at 7.30 a.m., dressed in my bright colours and wearing my favourite floral perfume, I returned to the surgery. Doctor Steven and John Smith were chatting in the staff room when I went in. Their greetings couldn't have been warmer.

"You were missed," Dr. Steven said. "It's great to have you back looking so well."

"In the pink and smelling of roses," John added with a smile.

I wasn't sure how much they had guessed, but there was no point in agonising over that. So I stood up in power mode, smiled and wished them a good day before going to my room. When I looked at my appointment diary it seemed as if fate was conspiring to test me. Helen Murray, was pencilled in at eleven, followed straight away by Paul Egan.

I immediately set about preparing myself for their negative onslaught. Going out into the tiny garden at the back of the surgery I grounded myself. Feeling both feet firmly on the earth I breathed deeply, charging each chakra in turn by imagining the rainbow colours powering them. From the bottom of my spine to the crown of my head I visualised red, orange, yellow, green, blue, indigo and violet invigorating my power centres. I also imagined the positive emotions of love, compassion, gentleness and kindness filling my body right down to the soles of my feet. Then I forcefully exhaled all anxiety, fear, grief, worry, and tiredness. When I had breathed in this way a number of times I acted "as if" by assuming the pose of a very confident professional, and returned to the surgery repeating "I'm strong and capable."

When Helen came in I greeted her with a big smile.

"I'm glad to see you back doctor," she said. "Had you a nice break?"

"I was attending a course in complementary therapies," I replied. "It was very interesting."

"Would that help me?" she asked and then added her usual addendum "because I'm still feeling as bad as ever!"

I looked at her, I mean really looked at her for the first time in a long time. Chronologically I knew that she was only three years older than Tara, but biologically they were multiples of that apart. She sat with her shoulders rounded and her head down. Her hair was dull and thin, her skin rough and blotchy. There was no sparkle about her. Every movement was laborious. Of course she would attribute most of this to her condition. I believed it was as a consequence of the mismanagement of her condition. I was certain, that despite her protests, she wasn't sticking to her diet, or exercising. But then, rather than regarding her with annoyance and disappointment as I usually did, I tried to empathize with her. The words of the Psalm came to mind and I attempted to look at her with compassion; with gentleness and kindness. After all I didn't know enough about her circumstances to judge her. In her situation perhaps I'd have been the very same. This change in attitude made an amazing difference. When I looked out at the world through her eyes all I could see was more of the same; not a very thrilling prospect. In the four years since she had become my patient I had never heard her mention an exciting trip, or a fun experience, or a purpose other than going to work.

"I'd like to ask your help Helen," I began not really sure how this was going to finish.

She perked up and looked interested.

"I'd be very grateful if you could help me to conduct an experiment. It will mean you having to come to the surgery for a few minutes every Wednesday for the next couple of weeks. Would that be possible?"

"What's the experiment doctor?"

"It's to determine if complementary medicine could help in the treatment of diabetes," I explained, not knowing where this idea had come from. "Of course you are completely free to refuse, and I'll understand if you do."

"Oh no. doctor," she interrupted. "I'd be happy to help. What would I have to do?"

"You would have to undertake to incorporate certain strategies into your life and to report back to me on your progress. Would that be possible?"

"No problem," she replied.

As soon as she had closed the surgery door there was a knock on it. When she popped her head in, in answer to my "Yes" I was sure that she had had second thoughts. "Will it hurt?" she asked.

"No," I replied beckoning her to come back in. "It's all about using the good vibrations of love, light, and laughter to heal. Sit down," I said indicating a chair while I took out the readings on love which we had received at the first session. "Have a look at these," I suggested. "See what you think."

When she had read the first one, St Paul's letter to the Corinthians, she immediately brought the second sheet, containing Nelson Mandela's speech, to the top.

"What do you think?" I asked when she had finished reading. She didn't speak; just looked at me, smiled, nodded, got up quickly and left.

Before going into the waiting room to invite Mr. Egan into the surgery, I took a few deep breaths and repeated my mantra numerous times. When he came in, complaining of back pain, I applied the same strategy which I had used to such good effect with Helen. I tried to look at him with gentleness and kindness, and once again this changed my perspective. Instead of viewing him as a grumpy, awkward individual, I now saw an elderly, lonely man. I repeated the invitation which I had extended to Helen. He dismissed the idea practically before I had articulated it.

"I wouldn't have time to come here every Wednesday," he said scornfully. "I have things to do."

That's fine Mr. Egan," I replied. "It's really important to have something to do, something to look forward to, and someone to love."

"Yeah," he said very gruffly, as he took his prescription and left.

I felt as if he had kicked me in the stomach. All the positivity threatened to evaporate in a puff of smoke. The old doubts threatened to return. I took out the course notes and reread them while picturing the huge change in Tara. That helped, somewhat.

When Rob called that evening he had a map of the Camino and a book that he'd borrowed from the library. He was all gung-ho and full of plans. He'd obviously done a lot of research. He informed me that people have walked the pilgrim route for over 1,000 years. That according to legend they are walking to the tomb of St. James, the Apostle, and Patron Saint of Spain. That after Rome and Jerusalem it is the third most visited site in Christendom. He knew that the French Route was799 kilometres, (490 miles) and would take approximately five weeks to complete. When he saw my reaction to that he added hastily that we could do it in stages. We could, he said, fly to Biarritz in south eastern France, and travel by train from there to St Jean Pied de Port on the French side of the Pyrenees which is the starting point of the walk known as the Camino Francaise.

On the first day of our hike we would cross into Spain on the route which the French Leader, Napoleon, and his army had taken on their journey to conquer that country. He described the Augustinian Abbey at the top of the mountains where we would spend our first night. The names of the Spanish towns rolled off his tongue as if he were familiar with them. Pamplona, home of the annual bull run made famous by Hemingway in his novel "The Sun Also Rises;" Puenta la Reine, Estella, Viana, where Cesare Borgia, son of the Borgia Pope Alexander VI is buried, Santo Domingo de la Calzada where two live chickens live in the Cathedral to commemorate a miracle performed by its patron, Santo Domingo, and we could, he added with great excitement, visit the tomb of El Cid in the Cathedral in Burgos. He was in full flight.

"That sounds wonderful Rob," I interrupted. "But I've only just come back from four weeks holidays, so I can't really ask for more time off."

"Oh I know. I don't mean to put pressure on you. But it's important to have something to look forward to, and a reason to keep in good shape."

While I was feeling a little more energetic I knew I still had a long way to go before I could face the challenge which Rob was proposing. But it did sound wonderful. I could imagine the fabulous Spanish sunshine, the feeling of freedom, and the fun and the camaraderie of other like-minded people. We had experienced those things on previous long-distance hikes. This would be fantastic too.

"I'll loan you the book. You might like to have a look at it," he said, leaving "The Way of Saint James" on the worktop as he went out.

When I took up the paperback it fell open at the start of the last chapter. This was a well-thumbed section and made interesting reading. Beneath a picture of the Gothic Cathedral of Santiago de Compostella the rituals long associated with the walk were detailed. It explained that so many millions of pilgrims have touched the massive marble pillar inside the main door of the Basilica that it now bears the indentation marks of their fingers. That it is traditional to put one's forehead against that of the statue of the genius, Maestro Mateo, who sculpted this column, in the hope of accessing some of his brilliance. That one then proceeds to climb the steps behind the beautifully carved altar to hug the golden, jewel encrusted figure of Saint James who presides over the Cathedral, before finally praying at the silver casket in the crypt which contains his body. It sounded magical. I wanted to go there. I determined that I would as I breathed in deeply and drank my positively charged water.

On Friday Rob rang the surgery. Immediately alarm bells went off. He never contacted me at work.

"What time are you finished at?" he asked.

"My last appointment is at five thirty."

"Can I meet you then? It's important. I've something to tell you."

"Can you give me a clue?"

"No, I'll explain when I see you."

126

My interest was peaked. I couldn't imagine what it was. But I got the feeling that the news was not good.

"Ok Rob," I agreed checking the clock. I had to wait another four hours to find out what was up.

"Where will we meet?"

I was expecting him to suggest Nice Bites. It was the restaurant nearest the surgery.

"I'll see you in The Castle," he said.

"Why way out there Rob?" I asked. The hotel was a good 6 km. (5 miles) outside the town.

"I'll explain later."

I didn't go to The Castle. There was no need to. As soon as I drove up the street I knew the reason for Rob's call. Peter was home. He was coming out of Byrne's as I passed. He looked very well. Australia was obviously agreeing with him. The last time I'd seen him was in church on Christmas morning and all I'd seen then was the back of his head before I'd made a quick exit.

I drove home to my empty house. Even then, a few months after Lucy's death, I still had to remind myself that I didn't have to call her. That she wasn't at home waiting to have a chat. When I went into the kitchen her photo was smiling at me from the counter. It was her favourite one. The one Peter had taken the day we'd brought her on the steam train from Mullingar to Tullamore. The memory of that day conjured up so many recollections. Thoughts of when she and Peter were both still in my life. Things had been so totally different then. I was busy working on the house and happily planning our wedding. With my two bridesmaids, Lucy and Louise, I attended every wedding fair within a 100 kilometre, (60 mile) radius of home. We had so much fun sampling menus, trying on dresses and having our hair and makeup done. Peter rarely came along. He always had something very important to do. It was Lucy who, with her childlike candour, highlighted the problem which I wasn't prepared to admit to. Peter didn't want to commit.

"Rachael, when are you getting married?" she had asked emphasising the "when." We were on our way to yet another wedding fair in Athlone. I knew by the expression on Louise's face that she felt uncomfortable with Lucy's question.

"Soon," I said.

"Great I can't wait to be a bridesmaid and wear a big fancy bridesmaid's dress like the ones on the tele," she said smiling one of her brightest smiles which creased up her eyes and puffed out her little cheeks. My heart went out to her. I loved her so much.

That was how I was feeling too. I couldn't wait to get married and Peter should have been feeling the same way.

"How stupid am I? How can any of this stuff help me?" I asked looking around the kitchen. The water filter jug was sitting on a card on which the words; love, thanks, beauty, Mam, Dad, energy and joy were written. Large pieces of coloured cloth were draped over the chairs where I had put them the precious night, and although it was only a few days since I had tried to convince Liz of the power of positive affirmations I felt that no amount of repeating them would help me then. "And you're going to put more pressure on yourself driving up to Bray and back again in the one night for the next few weeks to hear more of the same? I don't think so," I said as I got up and opened a bottle of red wine.

"Where are you? Are you ok?" Rob asked when I eventually answered the 'phone.

"I know about Peter," I replied.

"I was afraid of that," he said. "When you didn't show I was worried about you."

"I'm alright," I said, so consumed with self-pity that I didn't care about the worry I had caused him. I didn't even apologise. I just poured myself another glass of wine.

Luckily, I had the next day off. Saturdays off were very rare and very special, so I always made plans to make the most of them. That Saturday I had intended to surprise my godchild Colm by bringing him

128

to the zoo. I knew he'd love it. A new baby elephant had arrived and Colm loved elephants. Every time one appeared on the television he squealed with delight. Luckily I hadn't mentioned my plans to him because when I woke on Saturday morning, sprawled out in the armchair in the kitchen still fully dressed, my head was thumping, and I knew I was in no condition to drive. I felt dreadful. When I looked in the mirror my old self looked back at me. "What's the point?" I asked. "Who cares?"

The gentle tap on the window made me jump. I knew it had to be Rob. I got down on all fours and started to crawl towards the hall.

"I know you're there Rachael," he said. "I can see you."

At that point I'd have been happy if the floor had opened up and swallowed me. I felt so mean and so foolish.

When I let him in he didn't ask anything. He didn't need to.

"Sit down, I'll make you a cup of tea," he said going to the sink to fill the kettle. The water jug was on the draining board.

"What's this Rachael?" he asked lifting up the piece of card which was covered in positive words.

When I explained he replaced the jug on it.

"I must try that," he said. "Sure if it doesn't work it won't do me any harm. Has the colour to do with the course as well?" he asked indicating the furniture.

I nodded.

When I had filled him in on the logic behind that he nodded approvingly.

"Well it certainly makes the place look very cheerful," he said before asking if there were any other strategies which might help him.

"No Rob," I said. "In fact I think you could actually give the course."

He laughed. "What do you mean Rachael?"

"Well it's all about being positive, and you're a master at that. But for me at the moment Rob it's very tough. Sometimes I think it takes more effort than its worth."

"I wouldn't say that," he replied. "What's the alternative?"

"I don't know," I said.

129

"Well did this help?" he asked placing the empty wine bottle in the recycling bin.

I shook my head. "But maybe the course can't help either. I don't know whether it's worth continuing with or not because?"

"Well it certainly won't help if you don't attend," he said forcibly, cutting in on me. "What have you to lose? A few hours once a week for the next couple of weeks. And look what you're gaining; you're meeting new people and are being made aware of new stuff and broadening your knowledge base. Go on Rachael, you're not a quitter. Give it a try," he said pouring the tea before taking his favourite biscuits out of the press.

SOUND VIBRATIONS

On the following Tuesday at six thirty Rob rang. "I'm just ready to go," I said before he asked.

"That's the spirit Rachael," he said. "An open mind must precede all great breakthroughs."

I had to smile. Rob always had an appropriate quote to support any point he wanted to make. I was sure he made half of them up.

On the journey to Bray I wondered what that evening's topic could possibly be. We had already examined the healing vibrations of; love, air, water, nutrition, light, colour and perfume. As soon as Tara had welcomed us she indicated that that evening we would explore the power of sound vibrations.

"The programme which I am going to play for you communicates this better than I ever could," she said turning up the volume on her laptop.

"Good evening, and welcome to this, the second and final programme in our series on the power of sound," the presenter said in his beautifully modulated voice. "In studio tonight we have Mr. Thomas Dowling, who is a lecturer in biblical studies. He is once again joined by writer and scientist, Professor Elizabeth Ward, and Dr. Leo Ivers, medical practitioner and yoga teacher. In response to the huge number of calls generated by last week's discussion, I wish to remind you that the entire programme is available on the station's website at www.Scienceisknowledge.ie. But for the benefit of those listeners who haven't access to the internet, I will recap on some of the more salient points.

Starting literally at the beginning, we found proof of the power of sound as the source of all creation. This phenomenon, described by scientists and physicists as The Big Bang, attributes the universe to a force powered by a thunderous noise. We found that this theory is supported by both Eastern and Christian teachings. In the Hindu tradition creation is believed to have been powered by the sound of the sacred Aum. While in his gospel John writes; "In the beginning was the

Word, and the Word was with God, and the Word was God. The same was in the beginning with God. All things were made by Him; and without him was made nothing that was made." Again in Chapter 1:14 John refers to God as the Word: "And the Word was made flesh and dwelt amongst us."

We heard that great religious teachers have always stressed the importance of the word in the pursuit of happiness and health. Buddha taught that kind and helpful words help one to reach Nirvana; right speech being one of the steps of the Noble Eightfold Path which leads to bliss. And Jesus cautioned; "That which goes into a man's mouth does not make him unclean, but that which comes out of his mouth makes him unclean."

We also made reference to the limitless potential of the word for good or evil," he continued. "We acknowledged that once released, no force on earth can contain it, that its strength never lessens or wanes. Indeed its power is increased by repetition, rather than diminished by it. While acknowledging the power of a demeaning word to devastate the spoken to, there was also the suggestion that negative speech impacts on the speaker. Dr. Elizabeth reminded us that the untrue word effects bodily chemistry to such an extent that it is measurable on a lie detector machine. This, she suggested, was possibly due to an instinctive recoiling by the body. Quite simply she believes that because we are intrinsically good, the body tries to distance itself from the wrongdoing, in this case the lie. Her observation prompted a discussion as to the possible ill effects that the spoken obscenities and foul language, so commonplace in today's culture are having on us. Are they also causing our bodies, on some level, to recoil in horror, depriving us of vital life giving energy both on a personal and global level? we asked. While the answer to this question is currently unavailable as a scientific certainty, there was a general consensus here in the studio that this may well be so.

Then we engaged in a very simple experiment which serves to prove the power of the word to create our reality. I will now repeat it for the benefit of anyone who missed last week's programme. Stand with the eyes closed and an arm extended at shoulder level," he directed. "Now repeat ten times, I'm weak, I'm weak, I'm weak. Then invite someone to place one hand on your shoulder, and the other on your wrist and to try to push the arm down. Now once again stand up straight. Stretch the arm out at shoulder level. Close the eyes and repeat ten times; "I'm strong, I'm strong, I'm strong." Proceed as before and see what happens," he urged.

We looked around at one another and smiled remembering the effect that this experiment had had on us, when Tara had demonstrated it on the first night of the course.

"It is very obvious from this how powerful words are," he warned. "They must be used with discretion. Dr. Ivers gave us some very good advice worth repeating: he urged us to ensure that the little voice in our heads was always an optimistic, happy one.

While last week's programme acknowledged the power of all words, we found that some have traditionally been seen as of greater significance and importance than others," the presenter continued. "The name of God is one such word. The Bible tells us to use this name with respect. "Hallowed be thy name," Jesus prayed to the Father. And Scripture advises how it should not be used. "Thou shalt not take the name of the Lord thy God in vain," God dictated to Moses.

For both Hindus and Buddhists Aum is considered a sacred sound," he continued. "This most powerful of holy words is seen as the root of all things. They believe that chanting, or meditating on it, enables them to expand their consciousness and to commune with the divine.

Finally, last week we learned that our voices and our words are as distinctive as our finger prints. They define us. They are part of what we are. This is true we were informed, not only on a personal level, but also on a national one. We learned that each language has its own particular frequency. The frequency of the French language is between 1,000 and 2,000Hz, the Japanese between 150Hz.-1,500Hz. while the English language has a frequency of between 2,000 and 12,000Hz."

The old Irish proverb "Tír gan teanga, tír gan anam," immediately came to my mind. "A country without a language is a country without a soul." "Perhaps it is true," I thought. "Perhaps our national soul is diminished by the fact that our language, one of the oldest and most melodic in Europe, is now seldom heard. Is that why we are so maudlin? Is the Irish Nation missing an essential frequency? Could this explain the great Irish melancholia? On the other hand is it the reason why children educated through the medium of Irish were, on average, better achievers?" I scanned the faces of the group to see their reaction to this information but everyone appeared deep in thought, giving the programme their full attention. I however resolved to start listening to and watching Irish language programmes on radio and television in the hope that it would satisfy the innate need to hear my own native tongue.

"Now, in tonight's programme, we are going to discuss some very dramatic historical incidences which appear to demonstrate the power of sound," the presenter continued. "Mr. Dowling, your example from the Bible, is truly a very remarkable one. It is a story, which I'm sure, the majority of our listeners are familiar with, but whose significance in this context may well have escaped them."

"That is correct. As children, most of us would have sung of Joshua and the battle of Jericho without giving any serious consideration to the source of the power which destroyed that city. We knew that the walls came tumbling down, but most likely never sought an explanation as to how this happened."

"For those of us who are not as familiar as you with this story, will you please remind us of it," the host prompted.

Mr. Dowling cleared his throat with a gentle, "Ahem," and continued.

"After forty years wandering in the desert, the tribe of Israel was literally within sight of the Promised Land. They could actually see it from Mount Nebo. It was only a three day walk away on the other side of the river Jordan. However, there was no rejoicing in their camp. Many believed that they, like Moses their leader who had just died, would never reach it. A formidable obstacle stood between them and the land which God had promised; the city of Jericho. It was a terrifying sight, heavily fortified, and surrounded by high walls which seemed to reach to the sky. The closer they came to it, the higher the walls towered above them. Undeterred Joshua, Moses' successor, led them on. When they had set up their camp at the outside wall of the town, he summoned his people. Then he placed them in marching order. The armed men led the way, followed by the priests who walked before the Arc of the Covenant. The seven priests immediately preceding it each carried a trumpet. The common people followed after the Arc. Once a day, for six days, they marched in silence around the walls of the city to the sound of the priests' trumpets. On the seventh day, before daybreak, they again set off. On that day Joshua ordered them to encircle the city seven times. On the seventh circle he gave the command; "Shout, for the Lord has delivered Jericho to you. Raise your voices, bang your drums, sound your horns. The Lord has delivered the city to you." Then the sounds of bugles, drums and voices thundered in the ears of the multitude. And the walls of Jericho came tumbling down."

We looked at one another in amazement. Obviously, as the presenter had said, we were familiar with the story, but from the reaction in the room it was clearly the first time any of us had viewed this wondrous event as an illustration of the power of sound.

"Dr. Ward," the presenter said turning his attention to the physicist, can science offer any explanation for this event? Is it possible that it could actually have taken place?"

"Oh yes," she replied emphatically. "In physics this occurrence demonstrates the law of resonance."

"Can you explain the principle of this law for us in lay man's language?" the presenter urged.

"Certainly, simply stated the law of resonance is the law which facilitates radio and television transmission, and 'phone and email contact. It is based on the principle that everything has a natural vibration, or frequency, and that everything on the same wavelength is connected. But as a scientist I find it amazing that a migrant people, wandering through the desert thousands of years ago, were party to this knowledge. In fact, their actions indicate quite a detailed knowledge of physics. They knew that for optimum performance, everything must vibrate at its natural rhythm; that any major deviation from this causes problems. There must be balance," she said stressing a point which Tara always emphasised. "A lowering of the natural vibration results in degeneration. An increase causes the object to oscillate too quickly and spin out of control, resulting in disaster. The Israelites used this knowledge to their advantage. Their over-enthusiastic noise making increased the vibrations of the wall and caused it to self-destruct. It's really astounding, when you consider that the genius accredited with discovering the law of resonance didn't do so until several millennia later, in the early 1900s."

"And he was?"

"Nikola Tesla."

"Since you have established a connection between him and my story, I'd appreciate hearing a little about him," Mr. Dowling interjected.

"Of course," Dr. Ward replied. "Unfortunately, in the short time which I have at my disposal, I can only paint a very sketchy picture of the man who was known as The Patron Saint of Electricity.

He was born to a Serbian family in a small village near Gospic in present day Croatia in 1856. He studied electrical engineering in the Austrian Polytechnic and at the University in Graz. In 1884 he went to New York to work with Thomas Edison. His work made possible the harnessing of Niagara Falls, winning him the title of The Man Who Lit Up the World, and The Man Who Invented the 20th Century. He was also interested in wireless transmission and posthumously, in 1943, the U. S. Supreme Court recognised his patent for radio as preceding that of Marconi's, thus acknowledging him as its true inventor. So, as you can see, his educational background and work experiences could not have been more different from those of Joshua. His first experiment with resonance however, bore many resemblances to that of the Israelites many centuries earlier. Who knows, perhaps he was inspired by them!

His experiment took place in his laboratory on Houston Street, New York," she continued. "He was seeking to prove his theory that everything on the same frequency influences everything else on that wavelength. The electro-mechanical resonators which he was using for his experiment succeeded in hitting the frequencies of many surrounding buildings. This caused them to shake and sway. The residents were terrorised. Panicked citizens rang the police department. It was only when he hit the frequency of his own building that Tesla became aware of the danger his experiment posed. He immediately terminated it by smashing the device before it destroyed part of the city of New York. He had discovered what Joshua knew thousands of years previously", Dr. Ward concluded. "He discovered that resonance in excess can destroy."

This wasn't the first time that I had heard the name Nikola Tesla. Many years previously, in the museum in Cairo, the tour guide had made a reference to him. As our group waited to view Tutankhamen's death mask, he entertained us by commenting on the many great mysteries surrounding the pyramids. He said that while all the experts were in agreement that, even with to-day's modern equipment, their construction would be deemed an amazing feat of engineering; they were divided on many points. There was no consensus as to their age, or on how long it had taken to construct them, or where the enormous labour force had come from. But they did agree that one of the greatest mysteries was how mere humans had carried huge blocks of stone, some as heavy as 20 tons, to build them. Many weird and wonderful theories had been advanced to explain this, he said. Some suggested that aliens had created them. Others credited them to occult powers. And then he added that the great scientist, Nikola Tesla, had advanced a theory, not far removed from that of the Big Bang. He was said to believe that sound had activated a power capable of lifting those enormous weights.

"I'm going to talk about the Tacoma bridge disaster," Dr. Ward replied when the anchor questioned her on the event she had chosen to highlight. "Relative to Jericho, this could be regarded as a recent incident," she began. "It occurred on the morning of November 7th 1940 in Washington State U.S.A. In that year, the year of its construction, The Old Tacoma Narrows Bridge was the third largest suspension bridge in the world. It measured 5,939 ft. (1,810 metres) and connected the Olympic Peninsula with Washington State mainland. From its construction the bridge had displayed a tendency to ripple in high winds. As a consequence it was called Galloping Gertie. On the morning of November 7th 1940, in a wind of 64 kilometres (40 miles) per hour, Gertie, which was designed to withstand winds of 193 kilometres (120 miles) an hour, collapsed. Miraculously there was no loss of human life. The only fatality was Tubby, pet cocker spaniel of local photographer, Leonard Coatsworth. When the bridge started to swing out of control Mr. Coatsworth abandoned his jeep and ran for safely to solid ground. Poor Tubby was less fortunate and died in the disaster.

This dramatic event caused shock waves around the world. Many of the people who had laboured on the construction of Galloping Gertie had worked on the Golden Gate Bridge, which also showed a tendency to sway. Was there a possibility that this disaster would be repeated? they wondered.

Happily, as we are all aware, the Golden Gate Bridge has not suffered the same fate. So what did happen to Galloping Gertie? What led to her destruction?" she asked. Indicating that this question has occupied the minds of many noted scholars over the intervening years she added that many theories have been put forward to explain the event, many of them based on resonance. Among them is the suggestion that the sound created by the wind whistling through the bridge's support trusses caused its downfall. Reports seem to suggest that on that day the characteristic flutter, or ripple, on the bridge was not consistent with other occasions. Formerly the bridge had rippled from side to side. On the eventful morning of November 7th it seemed to ripple from end to end. This change in direction was most likely caused by a directional change in the prevailing winds. Such a change could have

resulted in the wind creating a different sound to the one normally produced as it blew through Gertie's arches. Had the wind that morning
tuned into Gertie's frequency? Had its whistling increased Gertie's vibrations to the point of excess? Had Gertie also fallen victim to the
laws of resonance as the walls of Jericho had? As a crystal glass will
shatter if an opera singer hits the right note? And as ultra sound will
decimate gallstones?"

Dr. Ward finished her contribution without attempting to answer
any of the questions which she had raised.

After a few moments silence the presenter spoke. His tone suggested that he was still mulling over what he had heard. "It's actually
quite scary to think that something, which is so natural, such a basic
part of us, can, if mishandled produce total destruction," he said. "If a
discordant or too forceful sound can destroy large inanimate objects,
built of the world's hardest materials, we can only imagine with dread
the ill effects it can have on us!" The members of the panel murmured.

"Of course the power of sound has unlimited potential for good
also," Dr. Ivers said.

"Please elaborate on that Dr."

"We can harness its awesome energy, as displayed at Jericho and
Tacoma, and use it to our advantage," he replied very confidently. "The
power of sounds and words to heal has been recognised for centuries
by Yogi," he continued. "These healing words and sounds are called
mantras. They are believed to correspond with the lost chords of the
universe, hence their purported power to restore health and to regen-
erate. They work on many levels. By the very act of articulation they
are alleged to activate power or meridian points in the mouth, on the
tongue and palate. This results in a surge of energy along the meridians
which massages and energises the glands and organs situated along
their length. A message of wellbeing is then sent from the organs to
the brain. In turn, this positive change in brain chemistry induces feelings of calm, and leads to a relaxed state. In this state the body's own
power of healing is activated. These yogi mantras are based on vowel

combinations. They are sounded with the force of a full breath, and are said to heal and cleanse the body, and to increase energy."

"That magic word again," I thought. "Energy".

"But before I continue I must caution the listeners that these are very powerful words and should only be used under the supervision of a guru.

The brain, pituitary and pineal glands, benefit from the EEEE sound emitted through smiling parted lips," he instructed. "EA pronounced as in feather, resonates with the area of the throat. The A sound, as in mass, energises the area of the upper chest. The A of water resonates with the lungs. O strengthens the heart, stomach and liver. U as in you energises the kidneys. OO-EE energizes the rectum and sex glands.

For anyone who is interested in using these sounds as therapy remember my warning. Proceed very slowly and only under supervision. It is recommended that only two vowel sounds are repeated at any one time. An extra one may be added at intervals of four days."

Then he added that belief in the energising power of sound is not solely the preserve of yogi. "This belief is also the basis of the Sound Therapy advocated by Dr. Alfred Tomatis, the French ear nose and throat specialist," he informed us, adding that his research in the 1950s led him to conclude that the ears serve a dual purpose. He referred to them as "the body's dynamos."

His theory was that in the action of processing sound, the ear's Basilar membrane also energises the brain by vibrating all along its length, depending on the frequency of the sound it hears. Obviously then, the more vibrations this membrane is exposed to, the greater the energy produced. So, for optimum health and energy, Dr. Tomatis concluded that it is essential that the ear is hearing and processing every sound. He regarded any loss of sound as a loss of energy to the brain. His research reinforced this conclusion. He found that many ill people presenting to him were not hearing efficiently. They were missing out on many sound vibrations. Further research revealed a method of identifying the missing frequencies. The voice, he discovered, only reproduced the sounds which the ear could hear. By studying the recorded voice of his patient, and comparing it with the whole spectrum of sound, he could identify the missing frequencies. From his research he discovered that many ill people were not hearing the higher frequency sounds. Through the "Electronic Ear," a machine which he invented specifically for this purpose, he bombarded the ear with the missing frequencies. Because these higher frequencies, and more complex arrangements, are most often found in classical music, this was the medium that he used. As a result of this treatment the brain and motor function of his patients improved. When the hearing improved the voice also changed completely.

In recognition of his great contribution to the advancement of medicine, Dr.Tomatis was named Knight of Public Health of France in 1951. He was awarded a Gold Medal for Scientific Research in Brussels in 1958. The Tomatis Method of Sound Therapy is in use today in many centres of healing Dr. Ivers informed us before asking; "Can we too benefit from tuning into the frequencies of the world's greatest genii? By listening to Mozart, Bach, Beethoven, Mendelssohn, Handel, can we profit from being on their wavelength? Will their intricate, complex rhythms and melodies also improve our brain function and motor skills? That is a bit of research which you the listeners, can carry out," he suggested.

That remark definitely resonated with me. From what the panel had said I knew that I was missing the higher frequency sounds. I never listened to classical music. At home I had a box set of 50 CDs of the world's greatest composers, which I had received as a Christmas gift. It looked very impressive. I had displayed it strategically so as to catch the eye of visitors. An interest in the classical was good for street credibility I thought. But come to think of it, on closer observation it wouldn't fool anyone. The pristine box was still covered in cellophane.

"Chris, I realise that our time is nearly up, but may I just make two further observations on healing sounds?" Dr. Ivers asked.

"Of course, I'm as interested in hearing them as I'm sure our listeners are."

"Since the beginning of history, music and sound have been used to improve performance and health. Earliest man beat out tribal rhythms to incite passion, and to prepare for battle. Football fans and sporting enthusiasts encourage their teams by chanting and singing. Our National Anthems inspire pride. Rousing music energises, lullabies soothe. Once the music begins we are entirely at its mercy. Its magic is most definitely in its intrinsic ability to please. This allows us to transcend the present, and to relax and to facilitate the body's own healing process. It is precisely for this reason that music is being used more and more in hospitals and nursing homes. It is a powerful therapy. No matter how ill a patient is, he, or she, can still benefit from listening to their favourite music. With absolutely no effort, even the very ill can enjoy the healing power of sound. It is accessible to all.

Music is also a powerful antidote to depression," he added. "This illness is usually the product of a low energy state, resulting in a lack of serotonin, or dopamine, the happiness molecule. Music is an effective remedy for this condition because it encourages movement. It also affects the hypothalamus gland and turns off the stress response. So, when you're feeling the pressure from whatever source, it makes good sense to put on your favourite piece of music, and to sing along.

Besides music there are other sounds which influence our moods and our health," he continued without a pause, obviously trying to beat the clock. "The sound and action of laughter is a very positive vibration and one which we should try to cultivate. Laughter releases endorphins and promotes that feel good factor. Obviously genuine laughter is a mood elevator, but if you can find nothing to laugh at, pretend to laugh. Faked laughter can also benefit us. The very exercise of laughing relieves stress, and gives the internal organs a good massage."

The hourly beeps, which preceded the news, indicated that the time was up. The broadcaster continued to speak over them.

"Remember our ears are always on," he advised hurriedly. "So let's choose to hear and utter only what is beautiful. Let's tune into the world's greatest genii and most wonderful and energising sounds. It will help make our lives fun, happy and healthy. And remember to keep the little voice in the head positive. Good night and thanks for listening."

As soon as I got home I unwrapped the cellophane paper from the pack of classical CDs and played the first one which came to hand. Then lying back on the settee I perused the little information leaflet enclosed. As the beautiful strains of Handel's music filled my home I could feel my stomach tighten and my breath become shallow. I very consciously repeated, "Relax," to myself and concentrated on breathing deeply and slowly. When the nauseous feeling had passed I read a quote attributed to Ludwig Beethoven; "Handel is the greatest composer who ever lived. I would bare my head and kneel at his grave." This statement was most probably prompted by the fact that Handel had composed the Messiah in two weeks. That was incredible! For all my ignorance of classical music I was very familiar with the Messiah. Before that horrible day, many years previously, I had loved it and had been struck by its power and majesty. Now I appreciated it even more. It was composed in two weeks! Amazing! And even more amazingly, I could tap into the vibration of the genius who had created it in the comfort of my own home.

A quick perusal of the little book indicated that I had struck gold. By opening the box I had accessed the genius of the world's greatest minds. Mozart had composed his first work when he was five. Mendelssohn and Liszt were both child prodigies who had made their first public appearances at nine years of age. And according to the experts, by playing the music of Franz Peter Schubert 1797-1828, I was accessing the vibrations of one of the very greatest composers. Schumann, Brahms, Chopin, Tchaikovsky. The list went on and on. Because of one devastating experience I had deprived myself of the huge resource of brilliance which had been lying gagged in the box. If what the programme makers had said was true, and there seemed to be scientific proof that it was, then by tuning into the works of these masterminds I would be exposed to their vibrations, the vibrations of genius.

However the booklet also made clear what the panel had said, that resonance in excess can destroy, that balance is necessary. Many of the great composers had suffered from insanity and depression.

That night, before going to bed, I prescribed a course of music therapy for myself. When I needed to be creative I would tune into the vibrations of genius by listening to Handel, Mendelssohn, Mozart, Liszt, Gershwin, or indeed any of the great classical composers. For the times when I needed an energy boost, I prescribed a large dose of high tempo music. A rocking session would be bound to increase my sense of well-being and fun. And for all the other times I'd play my favourite country music. Then finally before going to bed I jotted down the most important points from that night's class:

Treat the name of God with respect.

Keep the voice in the head positive.

Sound vibrations are very powerful.

The ears are the body's dynamos: expose them to all sound frequencies.

Music is a powerful energising force.

Balance is vital. Anything in excess can destroy

At 6.30 a.m. the following morning I was strutting my stuff around the kitchen to the beat of the Rolling Stones. With a spring in my step I left for work taking with me ten of the classical gold CDs.

As I was parking Dr. Steven arrived and I waited to walk into the building with him. "Good morning Rachael. How are you today?" he asked getting out of the car and going to the boot to fetch his bag.

"Fine thank you," I replied, hoping to harness the power of the positive.

"I must say you're looking better. The sea air in Bray did you good. Just goes to show the benefit of a holiday. We're mostly like the man who was doing his best to cut timber with a blunt saw. When someone suggested that he sharpen it he replied that he didn't have the time. Some things are just too important to neglect."

It was true. I was feeling a little better. Of course Lucy still came to mind with the accompanying heartache, but when she did I made a conscious effort to adopt Rob's attitude. Rather than viewing her passing from my point of view I considered it from hers. She was now released from all the pain and discomfort which she had suffered. Her beautiful spirit was now free of the less than perfect body which had severely restricted her enjoyment of life. I was happy for her.

As was usual on a Wednesday Helen arrived promptly at eleven.

"How many more weeks are left on the course doctor?" she asked as she sat down.

"As far as I know we have three more sessions."

"Then that's the end of it?"

"Yes, that's the whole course," I assured her, hoping that her questions didn't indicate a waning of interest on her part. But I dismissed that thought immediately. It was completely contrary to what I had observed. In fact her enthusiasm for it had truly surprised me. From the word go she had seemed genuinely interested. Literally as soon as I had handed her the photocopies of Nelson Mandela's speech, and the Psalm on love, I had noticed an immediate change in her. She had read them straight away, probably anxious to see what she had volunteered for. But when she had finished reading she looked at me and I thought I had discerned a tear in her eye.

"You're looking very well Helen," I commented. "How are you feeling?"

"Not bad," she replied.

Her answer delighted me. It was a huge improvement on her usual, "Desperate."

"My partner, rather my ex-partner," she corrected "accused me of having met someone else," she giggled.

I didn't comment, as she continued; "I'm really enjoying treating myself each day to something that makes me feel good. Yesterday I bought a dress that's a little too small for me because I loved it. Now I'm determined to fit it. I never did anything like that before. It's amazing isn't it? A little kindness to yourself can make such a difference."

"Are you having any problems with the strategies?" I asked.

"No," she replied and to my surprise, as if checking items off a shopping list, she enumerated the things that she was doing.

"I'm being kind to myself. I'm breathing as you suggested. I'm drinking about two litres of water a day which I leave charging in a glass jug in the sunshine sitting on a card with the words love, thanks, home cooking, friend, peace, on it. I'm using positive self-talk, telling myself that I am brilliant, talented, gorgeous, and fabulous," she said self-consciously quoting the Mandela speech. "I'm trying to keep my space in order. In a word I'm being positive," she smiled.

"What's the lesson for today?" she asked settling herself into the chair and giving me her full attention. Funny I hadn't noticed how pretty her eyes were until then. Then it struck me. She'd had her hair cut in a fringe which accentuated them, and she was wearing a little make-up.

"What happened last night?" she asked.

"We examined the power of sound."

As soon as I said it she started to smile. The more I spoke the more amused she became.

"Are you alright?" I asked. It was such a silly question. She was very obviously alright; more than alright. Her face was totally relaxed, and her eyes sparkled as she silently recalled whatever incident she had found so amusing.

"I'm so sorry," she said when her memory of it caused her to giggle.

"There's no need to apologise," I assured her. "Laughter is a healing vibration," I repeated confidently as if I was the source of this knowledge, rather than it being something I had heard from Tara. "Would you like to share the joke with me? Laughter is good medicine."

"Your mention of the power of sound reminded me of something very naughty which I did to my neighbour," she said smiling broadly. My interest was peaked. "Everything in here is confidential," I joked hoping that she would share her experience with me.

"I'm very aware of the power of sound," she said. "I know for a fact that an annoying sound has the potential to destroy. So it's only logical to believe that a pleasant one has the opposite effect. I'm sure some sounds can drive people insane. I know they have that effect on me. I was actually driven to commit a crime to escape a noise which upset me."

"Oh dear," I thought, "what Pandora's Box have I opened now?" "You're not going to make me an accessory to a crime, are you Helen?" I asked shaking my head vigorously while still trying to maintain a smile.

"Oh no, nothing like that," she laughed. "Calling it a crime is an exaggeration. I hid my neighbour's wind chime because it was driving me insane. It was one of those heavy metal ones," she laughed again; "the ones where long steel cylinders hang in a circle around a big wooden gong. When I first heard it I had no idea where the dreadful noise was coming from. There was no pattern to it and no escaping it. When I could hear it, it was driving me mad. When it stopped I was waiting for it to start again, like waiting for the second shoe to drop. It went on all day and all night. I couldn't sleep. All I knew was that it was coming from my neighbour's garden.

Then one morning, after another sleepless night, as soon as she had left for work, I climbed up on a chair to investigate where the noise was coming from, and there it was, this huge wind chime, hanging on the other side of the dividing wall. I had never seen one like it before," she stressed.

Then she described how she had reached over and had tried to arrange the metal cylinders in a way that they couldn't reach the gong. Some of them she wrapped around the rope from which the whole contraption was suspended. Others she tied together, hoping that would stop the noise, but no. That night, when the wind came, the thing gonged happily and noisily away. For a number of days she tried to improve on her methods of sabotage. Nothing worked. Every night there seemed to be a storm. The chime was powered. She was powerless. She couldn't stop it. Sleep was out of the question. When it wasn't keeping her awake the anticipation of it was.

"Why didn't you ask her to take it in?"

"That's another sound bite, to do with her dog." she laughed. "You see I had already complained about his barking. From the time she left for work in the morning, till she came home in the evening, he never stopped. When I couldn't bear it any longer I asked her if she could please do something about it. So she left him in the house all day. But that's another story, involving torn cushions, chewed shoes and scratched paintwork. So Sheila and I had a history," she laughed.

"Tell me about the wind chime," I urged.

"Well after about a week of unsuccessful sabotage efforts I once again got up on the chair to see if there was anything else I could do. When I looked over the wall it was gone. But I could still hear it. For a moment I couldn't figure out where it was. Then I saw it in all its splendour, hanging from the circular clothes line in the middle of her garden, completely out of my reach. That was it! So to preserve my mental health I got over the wall and buried it in her rockery."

She laughed heartily recalling the incident. I had never seen her laugh before. Maybe I had never given her the time to laugh. Perhaps I needed to give my other patients more time as well. "Love is gentle,

149

love is kind. It is not arrogant or rude." The result of my being gentle and kind to Helen had rewarded me well. It had helped us share a positive experience and establish a bond which must help in healing.

"Do you think I'm dreadful?" she asked, still with a big smile on her face.

"Not at all Helen," I replied, and then I told her that I too had seen at first hand how noise can destroy a person. In a hostel in Yorkshire I had witnessed how it had changed a lovely, personable, mild mannered young man into a potential murderer.

"If you don't shut up, I'll kill you," he roared like a lunatic at a blissfully snoring Rob. Then, completely shattered, he took his sleeping bag and went downstairs to spend the night on the kitchen floor.

When I had filled her in on the previous night's class she left, assuring me that she would incorporate the healing power of sound into her day by playing a wide range of music, and by using only positive, beautiful words. I was convinced that she would.

MASSAGE

My final appointment was for 4 p.m. Perfect! I thought. That will give me time to go home, shower and change before leaving for Bray. Rose had invited me to have my tea with her. I was looking forward to getting to know her better.

While there was plenty of traffic on the road it was moving well and I reached the Dundrum exit before 6 p.m. Bray was only a twenty minute drive from there. However an accident on the south bound lane of the M50 motorway caused a standstill. I automatically pulled onto the hard shoulder, got out of the car, and taking my medical bag from the boot made my way to the scene, arriving just as the emergency services did. A young man's injured body lay on the road, having been tossed from a motorcycle whose wheels were still spinning in the centre of the highway. The passenger in the car was also injured, but not badly, while the driver had escaped unscathed. When the injured had been ferried to hospital I returned to the car.

I felt my stomach tighten, and my breathing become shallower. But on this occasion I didn't panic as I would formerly have done. Now I opened wide the car window and made a conscious effort to breathe calm in through my nose, and to expel distress out through my mouth, while repeating slowly and with intent, "relax, relax, relax." Then taking a bottle of water from my bag, I sipped from it, having first asked God to bless it with His calm and healing. When I felt sufficiently relaxed I rang Rose, explained what had happened, and made my apologies before continuing on my journey, arriving at the community centre feeling slightly tense, and ten minutes late.

Tara greeted me warmly. "Delighted to see you," she smiled. "We need all hands on deck tonight. We are going to practise massage."

Then as I made my way to my customary chair she continued; "As you are aware there are a number of complementary therapies which use massage as an aid to healing. These include reflexology, zone therapy, acupressure, neurolymphatic massage and touch for health. They are based on the ancient Chinese practise of Acupuncture. In all of them the fundamental belief is that illness and pain are as a result of an energy blockage, and that health is restored when the obstruction is removed. So the objective of all these therapies is to remove blockages from the energy pathways so that new energy can enter the area and facilitate healing. Tonight we are going to learn a little about these therapies, but before we do that let's just take a partner and experience at first hand the power of a simple massage," she said as she got up and stood behind Liz's chair.

Following her example Mike stood behind Carol, and David and Rose paired off together. This time there was no doubting it. David smiled as I passed by, and his red cravat gave him a dapper appearance. Sandra and I were to be partners. I was thankful that Sean wasn't there. I'd have been terrified to massage him. He came across as being so angry.

"We don't need any special instruction to massage," Tara explained as I wondered where to start. "It is a strategy which comes naturally to us. We use it instinctively. When we fall or hurt ourselves our immediate automatic reaction is to rub the hurt area. For now we'll massage across the shoulders and down the arms. Massage is very good as a prelude to working out," she said. "It is important to warm up the muscles to avoid damaging them. That's why I've scheduled this session before next week's class on exercise."

As soon as I started to work on Sandra she let out an involuntary "ouch." "Am I doing it right?" I asked Tara anxiously.

"Perfectly," she replied. "The magic is in the intention."

"Ouch," Sandra cried out again. She wasn't the only one. In fact all around me there were "Ouches" and "Ahs," but they were invariably followed by an, "Oh yes, that feels good," as we gently massaged across our partner's shoulders and down the arms coming off at the hands. After some time I could feel Sandra relaxing as her shoulders loosened up. She reluctantly changed places with me when Tara told us to swap over.

"Our bodies hold a lot of tension," Tara remarked. "We only have to listen to the expressions we use to be aware of this. We say there's a weight on my shoulders, or I've a pain in my face, or I'm sick with worry, or my heart is broken, or that something or someone has gotten up my nose.

In energy medicine many illnesses are believed to be emotional in origin, and are as a result of the body storing negative feelings resulting from unpleasant experiences," she said as she kneaded Liz's shoulders. But she explained that these emotional scars could be healed. And that together with deep breathing and exercise, massage was a very effective method of clearing out that negativity and facilitating the free flow of new energy. However, she warned that manipulating the place where the trauma was stored might cause a flash back to the disease-making incident. That, plus the fact that we were releasing negative energy into the system, meant that we should do it in a controlled way. A too sudden release of this energy could prove counter-productive. The body might become overloaded with toxins causing illness.

When we were sitting down again Tara informed us that there are fourteen meridians which carry energy to all the organs, muscles, and glands in the body, and that we can tap into them at a number of surface points on the hands, feet, face, and body.

"We owe this knowledge to the work of many distinguished specialists in the early nineteen hundreds," she said. "The first of these was Dr. William FitzGerald, an eminent, highly qualified, ear nose and throat specialist, who in 1913, introduced Zone therapy into the United States. According to his theory the body is divided into ten longitudinal zones loosely corresponding with the meridians, or the energy channels, of the ancient Chinese art of Acupuncture. Each toe defines a specific zone, therefore there are five zones per foot, and when the therapist works on one zone he impacts on everything on that meridian. In the 1930s and 1940s his body of work was further added to by Eunice D. Ingham and Dr. Frank Chapman. Eunice Ingham (1889–1974) was a nurse and physiotherapist who worked for the renowned physician, Dr. Joe Shelby Riley, a colleague of Dr. Fitzgerald's. She researched the zone therapy findings, and developed reflexology of the hands and feet. Her procedures and related practices are today used by modern reflexologists. In the 1930s Dr. Frank Chapman also mapped out the position of reflex points on the body. These therapies all seek to remove the energy blockages which are causing the illness. Once the blockages are removed the organs are revitalized, enabling healing to occur."

"How do you know where to massage?" Sandra asked.

"To begin with you just very gently massage the hands, feet and face," she answered. "Anywhere you feel pain, just rub it out. Pain is the body's way of signalling that something is wrong. Any area of pain indicates a blockage."

"If we are just massaging away sore spots how do we know which organ is ill?" Sandra asked.

"It's really not necessary to identify the problem area for healing to occur. Just gently rub the hand or foot and clear any sore spot by massaging it in a circular direction, or by applying pressure to it" she said, suggesting that we start by massaging around the neck of the thumb or big toe, followed by the tops of the toes or fingers, then the body of the fingers and toes, and finally the rest of the foot or hand.

"I don't think that it will be possible for me to massage my feet," David said in a very regretful tone. "I can't reach them."

"Not to worry," Tara replied. "Massaging the hands is also a very powerful technique David, and it is accessible to everyone, anywhere, and at any time. It is a wonderful healing strategy and can be incorporated into the day whenever you have a moment to spare."

"I think that would suit me better," he said.

"Anywhere you feel pain try to massage it out. Go slowly," she advised as she constantly did. "It would be unwise to try to remove all blockages at once. That would release too many toxins into the bloodstream at the same time."

"I'd love to have someone to give me a foot massage," Rose said. "I'm sure it's very relaxing."

"Yes," Tara agreed and added that it was also a wonderful way to strengthen a relationship. "But if you have no one to massage you, then foot and hand rollers are widely available and are excellent tools for manipulation," she suggested. "Or," she added as if it had only just occurred to her, "A very simple and effective way to give yourself an energy treatment is to roll your foot on a golf ball as you watch television or read. Pay attention to the areas where there is pain, and return to them until the pain has gone. Then you will know that the blockage has been cleared. But as I have said it is not wise to try to remove all the blockages in one go. Make haste slowly," she repeated addressing herself to Sandra as she handed her a small wooden ball covered with spikes, which resembled a miniature hedgehog. Sandra looked at it questioningly.

"It's a hand roller," Tara laughed. "It's a wonderful little gadget. When I'm out walking, or sitting in the bus, or in the cinema, I sometimes use this for a quick pick-me-up," she informed her.

"Am I using it properly?" Sandra asked as she rolled the little object between her palms. "There's no right or wrong way," Tara replied. "You can do as you are doing now and roll it between the palms of your hands, or you can use it on each hand in turn."

When Sandra passed the small wooden ball to me I did as Tara had suggested and rubbed it between my palms. That proved a painless experience. Yet when I concentrated on one hand at a time the pads of my fingers and thumbs were sore.

"Are there any questions?" she asked scanning the group, and stopping at Sandra.

She shook her head.

"As I said there are many points where the meridians can be accessed," she continued. "It is of course also possible to massage the full length of each meridian, and if anyone wishes to learn how to do that I will be happy to advise them on it. But conscious that people have time constraints, and that this is an additional exercise to be used in conjunction with the others, I have put together a massage which will take only a few minutes, but which will help to maintain the health of the major organs and glands by releasing negative emotions."

That sounded perfect to me. I had been wondering how I was going to work massage into my daily routine. It seemed as if I wasn't the only one feeling this way since I noticed heads nodding enthusiastically in response to Tara's suggestion.

"By massaging this point, the slight indentation in the forehead, we are stimulating the pituitary and the hypothalamus glands which as we know are essential for well being. When gently tapping here," she said placing her index and second fingers at the beginning of her eyebrows, "we are tapping into the bladder meridian and releasing trauma, hurt, sadness, restlessness, frustration, impatience and dread. This allows us to experience peace and emotional healing."

When I tapped the place which she had indicated it was very sore.

"We access the gallbladder meridian by tapping here," she said indicating the bone at the end of the eyebrow. "In removing the blockages in this area we are also removing the negative vibrations which may have caused the chakra powering this meridian to close down. As I have said in energy medicine many illnesses are seen as emotional in origin, so while improving the physical condition by freeing the meridian, we are also getting to the root of the problem and clearing it. The negative vibrations which register in the gallbladder are rage, anger, resentment, fear of change, and muddled thinking. The removal of this negativity allows clarity and compassion."

If pain was an indicator of emotional trauma, then there was a huge amount of stress stored in the area around my eyes. Initially I couldn't understand why this was so, but then it became clear. In my five years as a general practitioner I had been called out to the scene of two horrific accidents. I had also, on a number of occasions, witnessed other people's grief on receiving a devastating prognosis, or on the death of a loved one, and had had to make a conscious effort to hold back the tears. That these occasions should come to mind as I gently massaged my face, was perhaps in itself proof of what Tara had just said.

"By tapping on the bone directly under the pupil we can dispel the fear, anxiety, emptiness, worry, nervousness and disappointment which interfere with the proper functioning of the stomach. The clearing out of these negative emotions allows feelings of contentment and calmness to flow into our bodies. And gently tapping under the eyes, starting at the outside and working inwards, helps to stimulate the kidneys, and to remove fear. Please be very very gentle working in the area of the eyes," she cautioned. "Think of the pressure of a butterfly's wings, and make haste slowly."

By tapping into the little crevice under the nose and above the upper lip, she said we could release feelings of embarrassment, powerlessness, shame, guilt, grief, fear of ridicule and fear of failure. This clearance of negative energy would, she assured us, encourage the positive emotions of self-acceptance, self-empowerment, and compassion for self and others.

Then following her example we tapped on the depression under the bottom lip. By doing this we were releasing uncertainty, confusion, shame, and embarrassment, and allowing in clarity, certainty, confidence and self-acceptance. In the same way by vigorously massaging the collar bone point, just below the knob of the collar bone and next to the depression beside the Adam's apple, we again tapped into the kidney meridian and in so doing released feelings of indecision, worry, and general stress, which Tara said would be replaced by new energy to power our confidence and clarity. We accessed the lung meridian by tapping where the second rib joined the sternum and released feelings of sadness and grief, which were replaced by the positive emotions of letting go, and courage.

As Tara described the benefits of massage and tapping I found it difficult to accept that the simple techniques which she was advocating could possibly result in the major, life-enhancing changes which she was suggesting. But then I did as I always did when doubts about her theories came to mind, I reminded myself of how ill she had been, and of the near miraculous recovery which she had made.

She also advised that it was possible to maintain the health of the thyroid glands, which are located on either side of the windpipe, by massaging them gently in an upward direction three times a day. This she said would facilitate the production of the hormones necessary to regulate our metabolism, temperature and weight.

At this point I was beginning to feel tired. It had been a long day and I was finding it hard to concentrate. As if sensing my discomfort Tara changed tack completely, and with a big smile asked if there were any Tarzan fans there.

We looked at one another in bewilderment. What had that got to do with anything?

"Any Tarzan fans?" she repeated.

"Yes, as a kid," Mike answered.

"How did he get his strength Mike?"

Mike smiled and beat his upper chest with his fists while calling out "Ah, ah."

"Yes, the secret of Tarzan's strength was that he massaged his thymus gland. A healthy thymus strengthens us by manufacturing T cells, which boost our immune system and fight infection. Massaging our thymus will strengthen us too," she said. "Let's give it a try."

I found myself wondering how we would look to a stranger coming into the room, as we all massaged our chests and roared, "Ah."

"You can also give your body a quick boost by rubbing the ears vigorously," Tara said when the noise abated, explaining this by drawing our attention to their shape, suggesting that because they resemble the form of the foetus in the womb, they are regarded as the body in microcosm.

We all proceeded to do as she suggested. Very slowly I started to massage my ears. Normally the only time I paid any attention to them was when I was inserting my earrings. I looked around at the group. By the look on everyone's face they, like me, were feeling the pain.

I noticed Sandra. Beginning at the top of each ear she applied what looked like a fair amount of pressure along the whole length of the outer rims, pulling them out from her head as Tara had suggested.

With her eyes closed she was totally focussed on what she was doing, returning to some spots more frequently than to others. Finally, with her eyes still closed, she finished the exercise by giving both ears a vigorous rub.

"Any questions?" Tara asked.

"If someone had a very bad experience is there any danger in them massaging it out?" Sandra asked.

"No," Tara replied. "But it is important to make haste slowly, and to use all the other strategies as well; the breath, proper nutrition and hydration, positive self-talk, music and whatever makes that person feel good; whatever keeps their vibrations high." Sandra nodded.

"Before we go I'd just like to advise you that massaging the web between the fingers is very beneficial, particularly between the thumb and index finger. Give it a try," she suggested.

"Next week we'll talk about exercise," she said having checked that we had all received the course notes. Then, obviously in response to somebody's facial reaction to the word exercise, she added, "Don't worry. I don't intend to propose a tough programme. The secret is to find a way of exercising that you enjoy. That's the one for you."

Just before leaving she asked anyone who was free on Saturday to meet her at the community centre at 10a.m. She needed a little help, she said. Apologising for the short notice, and reassuring us that she understood that most people had family commitments, she wished us a good night.

Sandra and I walked to the car park together.

"Thank you so much for the lovely massage," she smiled. "I could actually feel myself de-stressing. I almost fell asleep. I wish Sean had been here. I think it's just what he needs. He's been through such trauma. We all have," she added as she got into her car. Her voice was loaded with emotion.

When we went into The Tea Cup Rose beckoned to me to join her. I had a quick cup of coffee and left for home, so I didn't have the opportunity to speak to Sandra again that night.

Before going to bed I read the course notes:

Scientific evidence of the importance of massage for good health:

"The scope of the science of Zone Reflex, (reflexology) is almost unlimited. Great physicians who have investigated it fully made the claim that it is the greatest ally yet found to their work. Side by side with other great therapies, zone therapy will stand in the march of science and progress."

Dr. Joe Selby Riley M.D., M.S., D.C., N.D.,

Poking and prodding the body flushes out toxins from various organs.

Dr. Frank Chapman, Osteopath, founder of the neurolymphatic points. 1930

Science is confirming what we know in our hearts, that as psychiatrist James Gordon put it; "Massage is medicine."

George Howe Colt.

Course notes;

Use hand, or foot rollers to remove energy blockages.

Massaging the ears gives the body a quick energy boost.

Tapping the face can help stimulate the major organs and glands: the pituitary and hypothalamus by massaging the slight indentation in the forehead, the bladder by tapping the beginning of the eyebrows, the gallbladder by tapping on the bone at the end of the eyebrow, the stomach by tapping on the bone directly under the pupil, the kidneys by tapping under the eyes, starting at the outside and working inwards. Tapping under the nose and above the upper lip releases feelings of embarrassment, guilt, grief, fear of ridicule and fear of failure, and tapping on the chin point, releases uncertainty, confusion, and shame.

DISORDER

Very conscious that I hadn't paid anything to compensate for either the course, or the tea which was laid on for us, I decided that despite Rob's invitation to go to visit a stately house and garden in Kildare, I would help Tara on the Saturday. Rose telephoned on Friday night and we arranged to meet at the community centre. We were the only ones who turned up, but Tara explained that she had heard from the rest of the group and that they were available any evening during the week if she needed them.

"We're going to help David de-clutter," she said inviting us to travel with her.

David's house was situated in a very nice area, about half a mile from the town centre. It was a detached bungalow, easily identifiable as David's. A large skip stood in the driveway. The grass hadn't been cut for ages and reached to the lower window-sill. Rose looked at me knowingly and shook her head.

Before Tara had even knocked on the door it opened to reveal a clean, but very uncomfortable looking David. I couldn't quite identify the look on his face until I entered the house; then I knew it was embarrassment. He was ashamed of how he lived. His house was a mess. It was full of clutter. Every surface, floor, table top and unit of furniture was covered with piles of clothes and black refuse sacks. Although it was in a dreadful state I felt it was an improvement on normal conditions. The large black refuse sacks were stuffed full of rubbish which I felt sure had, until recently, been strewn around the house. And all the clothes, bearing charity shop labels, had been arranged in neat piles on every available surface both on the floor and above it. A very narrow passage, the width of two legs, was all the access available. The curtains were drawn and a bare bulb was the only source of light.

He responded to Tara's warm greeting by thanking us for coming and apologising for the state of the place, no doubt noticing the disbelief and disgust which registered on our faces.

It's a disgrace," he said. "There's no excuse for it. I just didn't have the heart, or the energy to clean it up, and it got too big a job to handle. Somehow I just lost interest," he said looking around at the heaps of clothes and bags of rubbish.

The kitchen was an absolute disaster area. Refuse sacks were full of empty and half empty take-away food cartons, and heaps of old newspapers. While the sink was free of dishes it needed a good scrubbing, as did every surface, press, and utensil in the cupboards and drawers. Many of the tinned foods, on closer inspection, were well past their sell-by date. In a word the house was a disaster.

"This bedlam is really getting to me. I can't stick it anymore. I realise that I won't ever get well living like this," he said indicating the turmoil. "I have nowhere to prepare myself a good healthy, colourful meal, no comfortable place to sit where I can watch television, or listen to music. I can't have anyone in. I'm so ashamed of it that I'm reluctant to answer the door not wanting anyone to see the mess I'm living in. It's not as if I have so many people calling that I can afford to turn some away. I finally realised that I had to do something. Otherwise his words would be proven true. I can't let that happen again. I can't let him wreck my life, even from the grave," he said as Tara ran around opening every window and door. Then with her usual calm she stood back to appraise the situation, and even in the middle of chaos, she found something positive.

"Are these yours David?" she asked, pointing to a series of scenes of Bray which lined the walls in the sitting room.

"Yes," he replied.

"You're very talented. They're beautiful," she said with genuine admiration. "Is there any possibility that you could do some for me? I'd love a painting of the view from my front door looking out to sea."

"It's such a long time since I did any painting I'm afraid I'm very rusty."

"Judging by these, even your rusty work would be stunning."

"Thank you Tara," he said. "When I get the place cleared out I'll give it a try."

162

Tara and Rose were in charge of bringing all the clothes back to the charity shops while I attacked the kitchen with trepidation. I had never seen so many stages of decay in all my life. Some of the fungi were actually breathing. It was so disgusting. David was lucky he hadn't caught the plague.

Despite this I could hear Tara spreading positivity; reassuring him that it was a very good sign that he felt like de-cluttering.

"It's an indication that you're restoring order in your life," her words carried from the sitting room. "When we get the place cleared out we'll organise a work corner for you which will capture the creative energy in your home and help you to paint." I could imagine David agreeing.

At one o'clock we went to The Tea Cup for lunch, returning at two thirty laden with scrubbing brushes, cloths, washing up liquids and disinfectants. Many hours of scouring and cleaning later I finally stood in a pristine kitchen with white faced presses full of dishes which I would be happy to eat and drink from. Tara, Rose and David had also worked magic, so when we finally sat down to enjoy a cup of tea the house was completely transformed. David was visibly delighted.

"I can't thank you enough," he said raising his cup as if proposing a toast. "I know you won't be telling anyone that I'm a lazy good-for-nothing."

"Absolutely not," Tara replied emphatically. "What happened here today is between the three of us." We nodded. "And we'll have positive self talk only please," she smiled.

Then it seemed as if having cleared out his physical environment he wanted to rid his mind of old, ugly thoughts, and memories.

"See how deep rooted it is?" he continued. "See the effect he has had on me? That's what my father always called me, a lazy good-for-nothing so and so. You'll end up on the dole, mark my words. I can still hear him."

We remained silent.

"Someone at the A.A. meeting mentioned you," he said addressing Tara. "They said you had helped them. That's why I came. I need help desperately. I have loads of baggage, and lots of negative vibrations coming at me from this world and the next. But then that's probably no more than I deserve after what I've done."

When he stopped speaking he reached for his tea. Rose and I took our lead from him and did likewise. The ticking of the clock accentuated the silence.

"I had asthma as a child," he said as he replaced his cup on the saucer, "so I couldn't play football. That was a huge disappointment for my father. He was so proud of his physical prowess. Like my grandfather he had played Gaelic Football at the highest level and had scored for Wicklow in an All Ireland Final. I was expected to carry on the tradition, and he showed me no mercy when I couldn't. I was an embarrassment to him in front of the whole town, or so he thought. He blamed me for my physical limitations, and he berated my mother for making a "sissy" out of me.

"Why don't you put him in cotton wool," he'd roar at her when she'd insist that I wore my hat and scarf going out on the frosty mornings. The final straw for him was when I showed talent at music and art, two decidedly non-macho areas.

One of the most annoying things about the whole situation was that he was a perfect gentleman to other people. He was totally unrecognisable outside the home. We were frequently told by his workmates what great fun he was. Fun! He was no fun to live with. And, while he made no effort to engage with me, yet he still managed to be there anytime I made a mess of something. But it was because he was there that I did mess up. I was so terrified of him, and so afraid that my mother would be shouted at about the fool that I was. He was a bully. But as a child I didn't realise that. He was my father. I thought fathers were perfect, and knew everything. I took on board what he said, and believed every name he called me. In school, when I encountered a difficulty, I was a defeatist accepting that I wouldn't be able to solve any problem. After all I was stupid. My father had told me that, so it had to be true.

Although to all intents and purposes he would have been considered an educated man, in fact he was completely ignorant. He was totally unaware that he, to a great extent, was the one who was determining my path. The most successful people in the world in any field are not necessarily the most intelligent or talented. They are invariable the most tenacious. That tenacity, that belief that they will succeed, is planted in childhood.

I hated that man, and planned to escape as soon as I possibly could. Every penny I got I saved. Eventually I went as a foot passenger on the boat to England where my best friend's uncle gave me a job in his pub in Finchley. He trained me as a barman, and I happily settled into life there. I let my mother know where I was and that I was safe and doing fine. I also made it clear to her that I would never set foot in Bray again as long as my father was there.

I relished my freedom in London. Being in the bar trade it was easy to meet girls, and I made the most of every opportunity. Then I met Mary. She, like me, was an innocent abroad. From what I could gather her childhood hadn't been much better than my own. She was craving affection, just as I was. To cut a long story short she ended up pregnant. When she told me I made it perfectly clear that I didn't want to know, suggesting to her that the baby might not even be mine. Can you believe that? The poor girl was totally devastated. I destroyed her. Right there in front of my eyes I watched her disintegrate. Then the thought occurred to me that I was no better than my old man. I was a heartless bully, and he was right about me all along. That's when I started to drink heavily. It was a way of blocking out the truth that I was an even more despicable human being than my father. At least he had fed and clothed me, however grudgingly. Whereas I had destroyed two people's lives. Then I set about destroying myself.

Being a barman was the very worst occupation for someone hell bent on annihilation. I lost my job through drink and with it my accommodation and found myself on the dole living in hovels, and falling deeper and deeper into despair. I ended up begging on the streets, fulfilling his prophesy. I lost contact with everyone and everything.

It was many years later, when my father had passed away, that the Salvation Army found me. My mother wanted me to come home. That was fifteen years ago. We had a good ten years together, she and I. I joined the twelve step programme, and managed to keep on the dry until she passed away. Then I started to drink again, but it has nearly cost me my life, and I don't want that to happen. I want to stay dry. I want to make restitution for what I have done. I want to find my child."

That evening, as we were leaving, David invited us back on the following Saturday night for a "thank you" meal. When we protested, he insisted; saying it would ensure that he kept his house in order.

EXERCISE

I had no worries about the exercise class. I knew that I was reasonably fit. However I was looking forward to seeing what Tara would recommend.

When I entered the room, at about five past eight, the group was there massaging their arms and legs and warming up the muscles. After a few minutes of gentle stretching, Tara put on a disc of The Rolling Stones. "Satisfaction" filled the air. "Just go with the music and enjoy," she advised as her body gave expression to the beat. Everyone started to move, some more enthusiastically than others. "Satisfaction" gave way to "Jumping Jack Flash". By the time they started on "Brown Sugar" even David who had been very reluctant at the start, was shaking and grooving. At one stage I thought Sandra was playing an air guitar, but I couldn't be sure of that. I was too busy dancing. There was one thing I was certain of however; when the music stopped we were all smiling. And while I felt warm I was in no way under strain or exhausted.

"Exercising should be fun," Tara said as she shook her legs and hands in the manner in which she had instructed us to do when shaking off tired energy. "It should invigorate and energise. Its purpose is to renew and replenish the energy supply, not to deplete it. Dancing, walking, and swimming are all good forms of exercise. And remember that laughing gives the internal organs a good massage. Find an exercise that you love to do, something that makes you smile, and do a little every day. That way you'll be fit for life," she promised looking as lithe as a cat in her pink and purple leotard. "But if there is anyone who, for whatever reason, is unable to exercise, I would recommend that they do little stretches, even while seated," she said poised daintily on the edge of her chair.

"All healthy animals stretch. That's how they build up their power. They can't afford to waste their energies or exhaust themselves getting fit. On the contrary they must conserve their strength until they need to expend it in fight or flight mode. However it is imperative that they maintain their suppleness and agility. They do this by stretching and breaking down muscle tissue, which then relaxes, repairs, and becomes stronger. And in practising yoga we imitate their simple, strength building, stretching exercises, which are within the capabilities of most people. Yoga is very slow and relaxed. There is no pressure. Each person proceeds at his or her own pace.

In tonight's notes there is ample scientific evidence to support the value of exercise in maintaining health," she assured us holding up a bundle of photocopied sheets. "But what really convinced me of the effectiveness of yoga was attending a course given by a relative of Indra Devi," she continued. "When one of the students asked how long she had been practising yoga she replied, "Forty years." I was astounded. She was as flexible as a cobra, as supple as a cat, had beautiful skin and hair, and an air of tranquillity about her. When we asked how she had even known about yoga forty years previously, she told us of her relationship to Indra Devi."

I was just about to ask who Indra Devi was, when Carol beat me to it. Tara replied that she was the daughter of Russian nobility who had been forced to escape to the west after the revolution. Here she became an actress, and as such was able to indulge her love of travel. India was a country which held a particular fascination for her so she moved there and starred in a number of movies before she married a diplomat at the Czech Embassy.

Soon after her marriage she became very ill with a heart disease. Despite the best available medical treatment her condition deteriorated and she became an invalid, spending most of her time in bed. Purely by accident she met a yoga healer who cured her. This sparked her interest in the subject. She became the first western woman to teach it in India, where she was known as Mataji; the mother of yoga. When her husband died she returned to America and set up a clinic in California, teaching yoga to many of the famous film stars of the time. Elizabeth Arden became a devotee and helped her to gain recognition there. She remarried in the States, but when her second husband died

168

she relocated to Argentina at the age of 87. When she passed away in 2002, aged 102, the Argentinean papers described her as a "national treasure." Tara concluded her anecdote by adding that Indra's family were convinced that her good health, her attitude, and her zest for life were as a result of her yoga practises and consequently many of them became devotees of her exercise regime.

"There are many yoga exercises," she continued, standing up and beckoning us to do likewise, "But the ones I am going to recommend to you are similar to those which kept Indra Devi vital and fit until her death."

Then, asking Mike to accompany her, they left the room and returned a few moments later carrying yoga mats. These were placed in a circle and we each sat on one. There was a bit of huffing and puffing as some people had trouble getting down on the floor, but eventually we all made it and Tara started by demonstrating the roll, which she said was very effective for keeping the spine supple.

"When the spine is straight and supple we are young," she said reminding us of the exercise we had performed on the first night which illustrated that one simple spinal movement was all that was necessary to change the feeling from one of youth to one of old age.

"The health of the spine is key," she said as she sat on the mat with the soles of her feet flat on the floor and the knees bent. Then clasping her hands around her knees she rolled backwards and forwards.

"It's a rocking horse movement," she said her voice barely audible above the grunts and groans as we tried to copy her.

"Please don't force it. Just go as far as you can. It will come with practise," she promised as some of the group failed to muster up the momentum to move. When we had repeated this a few times Tara instructed us to rock from side to side, declaring this exercise as wonderful for anyone suffering from insomnia.

"The stretch is also good for the spine, and it aids digestion by working on the spleen, stomach, and liver," she said this time sitting with her legs stretched out in front of her. Then reaching down she placed the sole of her right foot against her left thigh. When we had copied her with various degrees of success, she effortlessly raised her hands above her head and gracefully lowered them, clasping her left ankle, while her head rested on her knee. She then reversed legs and stretched again. Then with both legs stretched out she once again bent forward and rested her head on her knees.

Looking at her in that pose she reminded me of a ballerina.

Then she rolled over on her tummy to perform an exercise which, she said, would stimulate the adrenal glands and boost our energy. It was also recommended as good for the spine and as an aid to digestion. She called it the cobra. It was performed by placing the palms of the hands on the floor under the shoulders. The legs were close together and the toes pointed. Then, while inhaling deeply, the upper part of the body was raised off the floor with the head back and the face looking at the ceiling. The area from the waist down didn't move.

Following on from the cobra, the locust produced similar results. It also helped the adrenal glands, kept the spine elastic and strengthened the abdominal muscles she informed us, as she now lay on her tummy with her chin on the floor. Her arms were by her sides and her fists were closed, with her thumbs resting on the mat.

"As you breathe in raise your right leg as high as possible," she said, demonstrating the movement. "Maintain that position while holding the breath before lowering the leg slowly as you exhale. Now repeat with the left leg, and then raise both legs together," she directed illustrating each move with the poise of a dancer.

"Just two more exercises," she said emphasizing how beneficial the twist was for the kidneys, liver, spleen, and the adrenal glands.

While I found it a little difficult to manage initially, I finally got to grips with it. In a way it resembled a child's game which I had played with Colm at Christmas. It involved sitting with both legs stretched out in front. Then, taking the right foot and bringing it over the left knee, you took the right toes in the right hand and put the left hand on the back of the waist with the palm facing outwards. You then inhaled deeply in this position and while exhaling turned as far as possible to the left. After a few seconds you returned slowly to the original posi-tion. We repeated this twice before performing it on the other side. Not everybody succeeded in twisting. But Tara assured us that that situation would change; that the philosophy of yoga is to proceed at one's own pace. That it is not a fitness regime; rather it is a system which encourages agility and energy.

"With that in mind I will now show you the shoulder stand," she said lying down on her back on the mat. "This pose, because it counteracts the pull of gravity, is purported to restore health and vitality, and to prevent ageing and wrinkles," she said, warning that anyone on medi-cation should check with their doctor before trying it.

Then she raised her legs and bottom off the mat using her hands to support her at the waist. She then lifted her back off the floor until her body was in a vertical position with her hands supporting her spine. Her upper shoulders and her head were the only parts resting on the mat.

"I don't think so," Liz said. "It might cure wrinkles, but I'd very prob-ably end up in hospital with a broken something or other."

"If you are unable to perform it you can still tap into its benefits by lying, or sitting down, and raising the legs," Tara advised. "And if there is ever a time when one is unable to exercise for some reason, research indicates that thinking about it can be nearly as beneficial as perform-ing it. And since these postures stretch the muscles, for optimum ben-efit it is recommended to lie flat on the floor afterwards to allow them time to relax and repair," she said as I happily stretched out to my full length on the mat feeling that I could have slept, but the clock was vis-ible and I knew it was time to go.

When Tara stood up I got to my feet. Mike and Carol bounced up effortlessly. Liz rolled over on her side, then onto her knees and up. With much laughter David pulled Rose up by which time Sandra was also standing.

"Of course exercising with a purpose is very beneficial, especially if that purpose is to help others," Tara said taking up her bag.

"If anyone here is from the country you will remember the fun and positive energy of the meitheal. [work party] And if you would like to replicate it please come here tomorrow night at eight. There's work to be done."

She made it sound fun and I was disappointed that I wouldn't be able to make it. When I explained that I was on duty she said that I would be missed, but that she would see me in David's house on Saturday night. "Looking forward to it," I said and left for home.

The next morning, when Helen arrived, I gave her the notes and explained the poses.

"I honestly can't see me being able to perform any of them," she said as she put the sheet down. "I'm really very unfit. I haven't exercised for years, but you knew that anyway," she added smiling.

"Is there any kind of physical activity that you think you would enjoy?" I asked hopefully.

"I love to dance and I've been bopping around the kitchen since I've started listening to music on the radio."

"Wonderful," I replied knowing without a doubt that the movement would help her both physically and emotionally. Then to encourage her further I assured her that within a short space of time she would be able to perform the yoga exercises. In the meantime I suggested that she read the instructions and visualise herself doing them because, according to Tara, that was almost as beneficial as actually performing them.

"I'm all for that," she said. "If imagining doing them can get me into my new dress, and get rid of some of these wrinkles, I'll be practising them in my mind for all I'm worth, particularly the shoulder stand," she smiled as I handed her a copy of the scientific evidence which Tara had given us to support the benefits of any kind of exercise, walking, dancing, swimming, stretching and yoga. After reading it I knew she'd be completely sold on the idea. Helen was a changed woman. She now wanted to be as well as she possibly could. While she read it I perused my own copy.

Scientific evidence of the importance of exercise for good health:

The February 2011 edition of Harvard Men's Health Watch states that regular aerobic exercise is the key for the head and the heart. That it not only can bring about remarkable changes to your body, but also to your spirits. That it has a unique capacity to exhilarate and relax, to provide stimulation and calm, to counter depression and dissipate stress has been verified in clinical trials that have used exercise to treat anxiety and depression.

There are several explanations as to how exercise can contend with problems as difficult as anxiety and depression; some chemical, others behavioural. The mental benefits of aerobic exercise have a neurochemical basis. Exercise reduces levels of the body's stress hormones, such as adrenaline and cortisol. It also stimulates the production of endorphins, the body's natural painkillers and mood elevators.

Behavioural factors contribute to the emotional benefits of exercise. As your waistline shrinks and your strength and stamina increase, your self-image will improve. You'll earn a sense of pride and self-confidence. Your renewed vigour will help you succeed in many tasks, and the discipline will help you achieve other lifestyle goals. Exercise and sports also provide opportunities to enjoy some solitude or to make friends and build networks.

Harvard Men's Health Watch notes that you should exercise nearly every day. "That doesn't necessarily mean hitting the gym. But it does mean at least 30 minutes of moderate activity. There is now good evidence of many physical and psychological benefits available to the population from regular exercise which should be recognised by all those involved in health care," it states.

"From physical exercise one gets lightness, a capacity for work, firmness, tolerance of difficulties, elimination of impurities, and stimulation of digestion."

Charaka the greatest writer on Ayurveda.

In his book "Perfect Health" Deepak Chopra M.D. describes walking as coming close to being the ideal exercise because it is a natural activity which satisfies all body types.

Rose and I had arranged to meet at David's house at 8 p.m. on Saturday night. Luckily she had arrived before me. Had it not been for her car in the driveway I'd have thought that I was in the wrong place. The garden was unrecognisable. The window-high grass had been transformed into an even lawn. Colourful shrubs replaced the unsightly overgrown hedge. Hanging baskets on either side of the hall door, and pretty window boxes gave the house a cared for look. Then it occurred to me that the transformation was probably due to the work of the meitheal which Tara had organised.

When I rang the bell, which was also a new addition, David answered immediately. I expected the rest of the group to be there since they had worked on the garden, but it was just Rose, Tara, and I. As the night progressed David informed us that he intended entertaining the others on the following Saturday night.

"I'm not used to having guests," he said. "I'm taking it slowly."

I noticed that he had made some changes to the house since we'd last been there. Not only was it as clean and ordered as when we'd left it but there were some added touches, like the small vase of flowers on the coffee table, and the lovely bright cushions scattered around the place, and the half-executed painting of Bray promenade propped up on its easel in the little sun room off the kitchen. Tara's eyes lit up when she saw it, declaring it just fractionally less stunning than the real thing.

David was a happy host, whistling as he served the meal. "I hope it's ok," he said. "I've been practising all week. I've had great fun trying out recipes from my mother's cook book. She'd be so happy to see me now, entertaining friends and using all the finery which she kept for good wear," he said indicating the beautiful china dinner service, Newbridge cutlery, Waterford crystal glasses, lighted candles, flowers, and linen cloth and napkins on the table. Soft music played in the background.

When we were seated comfortably he shared his news.

"I've been thinking for a long time about trying to contact Mary," he said looking from one to the other of us as if seeking a response. We allowed him to continue. "Perhaps I'm being selfish, but I'd like to know that she's alright. I'd like to know what happened to the child. He, or she, would be about forty now. I could even be a grandfather," he added incredulously. "I intend to proceed very slowly and carefully," he continued. "If I get the slightest inkling that my appearance on the scene will cause either of them any angst, then I'll back off immediately.

Of course there's always the possibility that I won't be able to trace them. I rang the hotel where Mary worked, but they reminded me that forty years is a long time. The place has changed hands a few times since then.

I've also googled her and come up with nothing. But I'm not giving up yet. I intend to keep trying. Enniscorthy is my only lead. It's the nearest big shopping town to her home. She often mentioned her father going there to buy and sell at the mart, and how worried they'd be when he'd disappear for a few days, and then the tiptoeing around, and the fear of upsetting him when he did eventually come home. I've driven around there a few times this past week; since I've gotten the house in order," he added with a smile. "I've had no luck so far but its early days yet and I'm not giving up. It's my only link with her. I intend to keep trying."

MEDITATION

The week after the course had officially ended Dr. Steven's only daughter was involved in an accident in Australia, and he and his wife, Caroline, had flown over immediately to be with her. Since John and I hadn't had the time to organise a locum we were covering for him, both in the surgery and on call out duty.

"Be thankful it didn't happen during the course; at least you're not missing that," Rob, always the optimist, said when I rang to cancel our arrangement to go to the cinema. He had been looking forward to seeing the film of the Camino for what seemed like an age. Since he had heard Martin Sheen being interviewed about "The Way" long before its release date, he had been waiting in anticipation for its arrival in Mullingar. I hated cancelling. As usual he took it in his stride.

"No problem!" he said. "I'm sure it will be out on DVD soon. That'll be even better. We can watch it with a glass of Spanish wine."

There was no fazing Rob. He went with the flow.

"But I'm still missing the group get-together, and I have been looking forward to that," I reminded him; the difference in our attitude to adversity now patently obvious.

As soon as I'd said it I wished I could take it back. It was so negative and so petty, compared with the reason why I couldn't make it. But I really was very disappointed that I was missing an opportunity to get to know the other group members better. Due to my long drive home after the course, I hadn't spent much time in The Tea Cup. Generally I just had a quick cup of tea and left. Consequently I hadn't gotten to know the other people in the group at all well. I had hoped that these informal meetings would give me the chance to do that.

Surprisingly it was David who had suggested that we should continue to meet up every Tuesday as usual, just to keep in touch and to exchange notes. These meetings were to take place in The Tea Cup at 8 p.m. and were to continue until we had our graduation, so to speak. At Rose's suggestion we had decided not to say goodbye on the final night of the course. As she quite rightly pointed out there wouldn't have been much time, and we all agreed that Tara deserved to be thanked in a relaxed and unhurried way.

While she had made no mention of remuneration we decided that we would each pay 120 euro, which was about the average cost of a similar course. While in my estimation we could never adequately compensate her for the wealth of information which she had given us, at least it was something. And we also included another 30 euro each to give her a present which we were all agreed she'd love; David's painting of Bray Head at sunrise.

"Let's make it a special night," Rose had suggested, adding that she would be very happy to have it in her home.

Since it was the holiday season it took a little planning to arrange a time which suited everyone. Finally it was agreed that we would meet up on the fourth Saturday following the end of the course. I thought that was a wonderful idea. It would be an incentive to continue with the strategies and by then they would be embedded as a habit.

The final session had been about meditation. Until that night I had never considered trying it. I believed it was a kind of esoteric exercise, requiring instruction by a guru, and besides I thought that I was too busy and couldn't spare the time. As if aware of my reservations, as soon as Tara introduced the subject, she dispelled my uncertainties on both counts. Rather than a mystical experience with religious conno-tations, she defined it as a natural method of stress release discovered by our ancestors. She traced its origins back to the Stone Age when, after a day's hunting, our forefathers tapped into this consciousness altering strategy while looking into the flames of the fire.

"We sometimes think that Stone Age man was free of tension, but in fact being a hunter gatherer he was constantly in fight or flight mode," she said.

She then explained that a body in this state produces cortisol and adrenaline which causes the heart rate to increase, the blood pressure to shoot up, the muscles to contract and tighten, and non-essential functions such as immunity and digestion to go by the wayside.

"Should this situation continue the health of the body is compromised," she said, adding that the ability to reach a state of meditation was therefore as important to Stone Age man as it is to us. That the relaxation which it facilitates enables physical renewal, where the muscles can relax, the heart slow down, where food can be digested, and the blood can circulate freely bringing nourishment and oxygen to the tissues and organs. She suggested that this altered state of consciousness is linked to higher levels of the feel-good chemicals such as serotonin, and to the growth hormone which repairs cells and tissue. That it lowers heart rate, boosts immunity, switches on the parasympathetic nervous system, and enables the body to thrive.

"When we are meditating we are on a different wavelength," she said. "Scientific monitoring of the brain indicates this."

She called it the frequency of peace.

"If we look at its famous exponents we see people who are the epitome of love and peace. Just think of the traditional depiction of Buddha," she said reminding us that he is always portrayed sitting in the lotus position with a smile on his face as he meditates. "And Jesus constantly went to a quiet place to pray," she added. "That's what meditation is. It is prayer. It is the part of prayer where we give God the opportunity to talk to us. It's the most important part actually," she added as if she was thinking aloud. "Unless we meditate we are not going to hear the answer to our prayer, we are not going to hear the advice and guidance which we have asked for."

As for not having the time to meditate, Tara blew that objection out of the water by quoting another peace loving exponent of the practise. Gandhi is reputed to have said; "I have so much to do today that I will need to meditate for two hours instead of one."

But it was her explanation of why she had started to meditate which really struck a chord with me.

"Meditation is the only medium which affords the body complete rest."

That resonated with me. I knew that some mornings when I woke up I felt anything but rested. Indeed I often felt exhausted after a night spent tossing and turning. This was particularly true immediately after Lucy's death. Those nightmares were thankfully less frequent now. That actually hadn't occurred to me until then. That was the way with the course. Things happened over time, slowly, gradually, almost imperceptibly, until something reminded you of the way they used to be.

She then told how she had gone about researching the effects of meditation, and had found numerous studies, conducted by eminent medical establishments, which proved that it benefited the health of the body.

"You will find them in the notes," she said before advising us that meditation should be undertaken in a quiet comfortable space, either before, or at least one and a half hours after eating, and that there was an advantage in always performing it in the same place so that on entering that space the body and mind would automatically know that it was time to relax. And while sitting in a lotus, or half lotus position, was seen as the ideal situation, she found that it suited her better to meditate on a straight backed chair, with her feet flat on the floor and her hands resting gently on her lap. Then with her eyes closed she just tuned in to her breathing. There was no effort required; and no need to change the breath in any way. All she had to do was to sit there, bringing her awareness to her breathing, with a gentle smile on her face.

She said that she had also found suggestions on how to focus more easily on the breath. One could repeat "in" on the inhalation, and "out" on the exhalation. Or one could count the in, or the out breath. Various books also suggested guided reflections, where one could record peaceful passages and then play them back during meditation, or one could repeat a word which conjured up a desirable state such as; peace, love, or health. The purpose of all these practises was to concentrate the mind so that it would not engage in energy sapping thoughts. As the breath flowed in, uninhibited by any tension, the body was free to relax and to heal itself.

Twenty minutes twice a day, preferably morning and late afternoon, were considered the best times. That made perfect sense. The first meditation set one up for the day's activities, while the afternoon session refreshed the body after the morning's exertions and left one invigorated for the events of the evening.

She made it sound exciting, declaring it as akin to a journey of discovery. "Frequently during meditation I managed to access information I would formerly not have known," she said. "It was amazing. Sometimes the answer to a crossword puzzle would come to mind, or I would know where to find something which I had misplaced."

At other times she experienced such wonderful calm that she was reluctant to finish her session. But, she reasoned, the purpose of meditation was to help live life more fully, not to escape it.

She informed us that the great artist, Salvador Dali, had used a type of meditation when seeking inspiration. He is said to have lain on his couch clutching a spoon in his hand. When he was so relaxed that the spoon fell from his grip, he would get up and paint.

"Now let's practise it," she suggested as I shifted on my chair to make myself as comfortable as possible.

Following her instruction I sat up straight with both feet placed firmly on the floor and my hands resting on my lap with the palms turned upwards. Then I closed my eyes, and wearing the smile which I used for my smiling energy technique, I tuned into my breathing. Almost immediately I thought of the drive home, and the patients I would see the following morning.

"If thoughts intrude just gently return your attention to your breathing," Tara advised.

That night my thoughts constantly strayed, but Tara said that this was normal and that when it happened one was to gently return one's attention to the breath.

'With practise you will reach a state of deep relaxation, where tension is released from the body on a physical level and your mind completely switches off," she said. That was definitely worth seeking.

The following morning when demonstrating the meditation technique to Helen I adopted the pose and repeated almost verbatim the words which Tara had used.

"If thoughts intrude just return your attention to your breath," I advised her, as if I was a seasoned meditator. It was ironic I thought, that when I had first invited Helen to partake in the course, I had had her interests at heart, but in fact her participation had helped me enormously. It had ensured that I kept up the practises, and I also found that explaining the strategies to her clarified them for me as well, a vindication of the theory that helping others benefits the self.

"Is that it?" Helen asked when the twenty minutes were up. Is that meditation?"

"Yes, that's it."

"But it's nothing," she continued looking at me incredulously. "When you said meditation I thought that something wonderful would happen, but it didn't. It's just nothing. Just closing your eyes and resting."

"But that's it Helen," I jumped in, not wanting her to be disappointed, or to lose faith. "It's because you're doing nothing that it's so effective," I explained just as Tara had explained to us the previous night. "It's only when your body is in that state of rest that it can heal itself. Look at these studies which support the benefits of meditation," I said handing her the copy of the notes which I had made for her.

As she read them, I read the master draft and knew that the research would convince any sceptic. It proved without the shadow of a doubt how life-supporting meditation is.

Scientific evidence of the importance of meditation for good health:

Research led by Dr Herbert Benson, associate professor of medicine at Harvard Medical School, showed that long term practitioners of relaxation methods like meditation had far more disease fighting genes than those who did not practise. The changes, say the researchers, were induced by what they call "the relaxation effect", a phenomenon that could be just as powerful as any medical drug but without the side effects.

A study at the Ohio State University found that progressive muscular relaxation, when practiced daily, reduced the risk of breast cancer recurrence.

In another study at Ohio State, a month of relaxation exercises boosted natural killer cells in the elderly, giving them a greater resistance to tumours and to viruses.

A study at the University of Western Australia found that women are more likely to conceive during periods when they are relaxed rather than stressed.

When patients suffering from irritable bowel syndrome began practicing a relaxation meditation twice daily, their symptoms of bloating, diarrhoea and constipation improved significantly. Meditation was so successful that the researchers at the State University of New York recommended it as an effective treatment.

A study at Harvard Medical School found that meditation lowered blood pressure by making the body less responsive to stress hormones, in a similar way to blood pressure-lowering medication.

Stress leads to inflammation, a state linked to heart disease, arthritis, asthma and skin conditions such as psoriasis, say researchers at Emory University in the U.S. Relaxation can help prevent and treat such symptoms by switching off the stress response. In this way, one study at McGill University in Canada found that meditation clinically improved the symptoms of psoriasis.

At the end of the sheet Tara had added her recommendations.

- *Meditate for twenty minutes twice a day, preferably morning and afternoon.*
- *Sit with the back straight, both feet flat on the floor and hands resting on the lap, palms turned upwards.*
- *Close the eyes and bring your attention to the breath.*
- *Breathe naturally; don't change the breath in any way.*
- *If thoughts intrude just return your attention to the breath.*

"Don't worry," Helen said when she had finished reading the notes. "I'm not knocking it. I believe you when you say it helps. There's no disputing this evidence. I'll definitely give it a try. "

Then before leaving, she thanked me for having given her the opportunity to participate in the course as she handed me a bound copy of Yeats' Poetry.

"I'll miss coming," she said. "I've enjoyed it so much. It has actually changed my life."

I was a little taken aback by this.

"That's wonderful," I said not really knowing how to respond. This was a development which I hadn't anticipated. There was no doubt but that she looked better. It was obvious from her appearance that she was taking better care of herself, and she was actually keeping a record of her blood sugar readings, something which she had never done before. But her effusive praise of the course had thrown me. This was the Helen who always had something wrong.

"I'm serious," she said as if sensing my ambivalent response to her. "I really mean it. The course has changed my life. It has given me dignity."

I didn't comment. Had I dismissed her words as empty praise I knew I would have offend her. It was clear that she meant them sincerely.

"I am the middle child in a working-class family of seven," she said, and I knew that it was my reaction to her comments which had forced her to explain further. I felt a little uncomfortable about that, but she seemed in no way embarrassed as she recounted how her parents had done a great job, and had expended all their energies on feeding, clothing, and rearing their children.

"None of us has ever been in trouble with the police, which is a great achievement for such a large family in the area where we lived," she said. "But our parents never told us that they loved us. That word was never mentioned. I'm not blaming them, that was the culture of the time. But I desperately needed love," she emphasised. "My life felt empty. I was never hungry or cold but there was a void there. As I got older I tried to fill the emptiness by reading every romantic novel that I could lay my hands on. Yet I still didn't know what love was. Had I been asked to describe it I'd have found it difficult to do so. But that morning in the surgery, when you handed me those two sheets of paper, I looked down at them expecting to find a list of rules and restrictions. Instead I found what I had spent my life searching for. On the top of the first sheet was the word love. That stunned me. I knew then with certainty that I had found what I needed; that I was on the right track. I knew that finally this was it. I knew this definition of love was correct, not because I was familiar with the gentleness and kindness which were used to describe it, but because I had experienced all too often the words used to describe non-love; arrogant, rude, irritable, resentful, wrong. In my adult life my deep yearning for love had caused me to hope that the rude, arrogant, irritable, resentful men whom I entertained would by some miracle change into kind and gentle people. This same craving for love had resulted in me allowing myself to be used for sex by the men I met in the pub. How could I have let myself be abused in that way?" she asked plaintively, a pained look on her face.

"That morning when I read the definition of real love I felt a deep sense of shame," she continued. "I tried to hide the tears by keeping my head bowed as I shuffled the pages, bringing the underneath one to the top. Once again words screamed at me."

"Our deepest fear is not that we are inadequate,

Our deepest fear is that we are powerful beyond measure, it is our light, not our darkness that most frightens us.

We ask ourselves who am I to be brilliant, gorgeous, talented and fabulous?

Actually who are you not to be? You are a child of God."

My eyes were continually drawn to those words.

"We ask ourselves who am I to be brilliant, gorgeous, talented and fabulous?

Actually who are you not to be? You are a child of God.

You are a child of God."

"That reading stunned me. I deserved more than I was accepting for myself. That was when I decided to end my relationship, a relationship which I knew would never prove loving. I was allowing a fine, strong, healthy young man, who was very capable of earning a living, to sponge off me. That wasn't what I wanted. I deserved better. I deserved love. I was going to have love in my life. I was going to love myself. I was going to be gentle and kind with myself, and I was going to start immediately."

Then she described how she had rushed home from the surgery, stood in front of the mirror, looked herself in the eye and repeated with determination, "I love you, I love you, you are brilliant, gorgeous, talented, and fabulous. You are a child of God."

Initially, she said, she had felt her body cringe in denial, but she had persisted. After some time she noticed her expression softening, as her pinched and puckered lips relaxed into a smile, and the tension lines around her eyes eased. Inside too, she had felt so much calmer, much sweeter. There was no further need for the aggressive attitude which she had over time adopted as a defence mechanism. She was a child of God. He would take care of her.

Her deepest regret was that she hadn't been aware of this years earlier. What a difference it could have made! It had never before occurred to her that she could fill the void in her life by loving herself. But now that was exactly what she was doing. And the more she supported her life through the loving strategies suggested, the more she valued it, and the easier it became to invest time in herself. She was worth it! She deserved the treats; her new hairstyle, the moisturiser for her face, a visit to the cinema, the body lotion, the lipstick, eye-shadow, perfume, all little treats, but so very life-affirming.

The course had changed her life. It had empowered her, given her dignity, and had improved her life condition, she said.

SOARING

The next few weeks flew by. It was hectic at work seeing my own patients as well as covering for Dr. Steven. But I tried as much as possible
to carry on with the course strategies. With a little planning I developed a routine which suited my needs. During the night if the demons
returned, I sat up in bed and brought my awareness to my breathing.
Then I repeated the words; "calm," "relax," or "peace". After some
time, when I lay down again, I invariably fell asleep.

Each morning before getting out of bed I invited all manner of good
things into my life. Then, while still lying there, I practised my deep
breathing exercises and tapped all the pressure points on my face and
chest. Once up I gave my body a good massage by vigorously rubbing
my head, arms, legs, tummy, and the soles of my feet. Then I stretched
and did the standing breathing exercises. After my shower I did my
own version of the healing smile meditation. Because of time constraints I just sat there and scanned my body. Then, having connected
with my little nephew Colm, I internalized the warm, loving feeling
which I felt for him, and directed it to any area of discomfort. I followed
this with twenty minutes of meditation, and sealed the energy at my
centre. This whole routine took approximately forty minutes.

When caught in traffic, or waiting in a queue at the supermarket, or
sitting on the bus, I sent love and thanks to my inner organs and to any
area where I felt stress. During the day, and whenever I had a spare
moment, I brought my awareness to my breathing only to find on occasions, particularly when under pressure, that I was not breathing at
all.

I drank positively charged water, blessed my food, and spent as
much time as possible outdoors. I kept the vibrations around me high
by dressing in brightly coloured clothes, playing beautiful music, and
having vibrantly coloured items in my home and on my plate. In the
evening, while my dinner was cooking, I performed my exercises and

evening meditation. I used my hand massager when watching television. When under stress I repeated the name of the virtue or the quality which I felt would help. This strategy had a very powerful knock-on effect. It resulted in me straightening up, and going about my business with a smile on my face. My smile invariably produced a responding smile from whoever I met and immediately the situation became a more positive one. Minutes that I would formerly have wasted I was now using to great advantage, and it felt good to be so purposeful with my time. It also felt great to know that I had access to the information which had changed Tara from a very ill, scared, and pathetic looking creature to the beautiful, confident woman she now was. And while spending so much time and energy on oneself might on first view be considered selfish, in fact the result proved to be the exact opposite. I found it benefited everyone I came in contact with since I was calmer, more patient, happier and felt more confident and capable. The advice on the aeroplane came to mind; just as parents travelling with children are advised to put their own oxygen masks on first, in similar fashion I was looking after myself in order to be able to help others. If we are not working well we can be of little assistance to anyone else.

Whenever I had a doubt, or a moment of uncertainty about the effectiveness of the strategies, I took out the course notes and reread the scientific evidence which supported them. This reassured me.

I also had a few rambles with Rob because, as far as I was concerned hiking was the easiest and most enjoyable way to apply the strategies. It combined air, water, food, colour, perfume, sound, and exercise. It also gave the internal organs a good massage. It was impossible to walk with Rob without having a good laugh. And it was also a great way of keeping in touch with the happenings in the town.

"I believe he's home for good," Rob said, knowing there was no need to identify the "he." We were having our lunch in the sunshine with our backs to the cairn on the top of Slievenamon looking down on the counties of Tipperary, Kilkenny and Waterford. "He's landed a job in Dublin. Seems he's got the travelling bug out of his system. What do you think of that?"

I honestly didn't know what to think. I had spent a lot of time discussing the situation with Louise. And at the end of it all I still didn't know how I felt about him. I didn't know if I could ever trust him not to disappoint me again. I didn't know either if I would ever be in that situation again. I didn't know if we'd ever get together again. But there was something I did know. My experiences of the past few years had taught me that it was only a waste of time to try to anticipate the future. The most unexpected things can happen. In the space of a few seconds your life can change without warning. So I was just going to take life as it came.

"I hope it works out for him," I said to Rob and meant it. Life was too short and too precious to waste by looking back.

I was really excited as I set out for Bray on the night of our graduation. It had been over a month since the last session and I hadn't been in touch with anyone in the meantime. I was looking forward to seeing them all and to hearing what affect the course had had on their lives.

As soon as I stopped the car outside her house Rose came out to greet me. She was tanned, smiling, and dressed in bright beautiful yellow.

"Oh it's lovely to see you again. We missed you at the Wednesday night sessions in The Tea Cup. You look marvellous," she enthused, standing back and surveying me, before giving me a big hug.

"You too," I replied truthfully. "You're a treat for the eyes in your beautiful happy yellow."

"I'm on Peter's frequency now," she smiled as we both turned to see who was arriving in the car which had just pulled up. As soon as it stopped we could hear the chatting and laughing before David, Mike, and Carol emerged.

"What a change from the first night in room two of the community centre," I thought, remembering the awkward silence. A lot of bonding had obviously taken place in The Tea Cup over the past four weeks.

"Come out into the garden," Rose said when Tara, Liz, and Sandra arrived. "We'll catch the evening sun."

It was a scene to delight the senses; an absolute treat for the chakra system. Red, pink, and yellow roses covered the walls, striking orange wallflowers and tall yellow sunflowers bloomed randomly here and there around the perimeter; the yellow St. John's wort had a luminosity which insured that it would not be overlooked despite standing in the far corner; vibrant blue agapanthus bloomed between the pergola and the water feature; the green lawn which stretched down to the river bank was as smooth as a billiard table; purple lavender emitted its exquisite perfume from the elevated rockery beside the swing, while indigo and violet hydrangea marked the boundary between the formal and wild flower gardens. Wallflowers, petunias, geraniums, jasmine, sweet pea, delighted the eyes and nose, contributing to a picture of every shade and hue imaginable.

"This has been my salvation," Rose said as I stood enchanted. "I spend as much time as possible here; breathing, exercising, meditating, and enjoying the beautiful colours and perfumes."

Rob again came to my mind. Perhaps that was the secret of his inextinguishable joy. All his working hours were spent communing with beautiful flowers, shrubs and trees, in the great outdoors.

"It was Peter's pride and delight and I nearly let it go to wreck and ruin," Rose continued, "but David and young James have helped me return it to its former glory." A smile passed between her and Liz. "Next year I hope to open it to the public during garden festival season and to donate the proceeds to charity. That's what Peter would have done," she said as she invited us to make ourselves at home, gesturing to the chairs which were arranged on the patio. But instead everyone chose to walk around the beautiful grounds.

From the outside her home was a very plain bungalow. At its time of construction, about fifty years previously I guessed, it was no doubt considered state of the art. But by today's standards it was a basic, functional, three bed roomed family home. However, if by virtue of its age it had lost out on the wow factor so evident in more recently built properties, this was more than made up for by the amount of space which surrounded it. This sense of space was most obvious to the rear of the house. The illusion was that the garden continued on for ever as it stretched uninterrupted down to the Dargle River, and then up the steeply rising far bank to end eventually where the tall trees met the sky.

"You could be in the country," Mike remarked. "You have complete privacy." Rose nodded.

The garden was divided into two areas. The cultivated space was a riot of vibrant colour. The other part, the wild flower garden, was equally stunning, if more discreet. Had Rob been there I'd' have remarked how like Hannah's Meadow it was. But since he wasn't I passed that remark to Mike who was standing beside me.

"I've never heard of Hannah's Meadow," he said. "Where is it?"

Then I told him of the area of conservation which we had come upon when walking in the highest regions of the Yorkshire Dales. It was by far the most beautiful field I had ever seen, covered with delicate wild flowers and native grasses. Hannah Hauxwell, after whom the meadow was named, had lived and farmed there in isolation for over forty years, without heat, water, or electricity. Carrying on in the tradition of her parents and grandparents she had never used any artificial products on the land; hence its unspoiled beauty. Her story came to light when a television reporter came upon her while hiking in the area.

As I recounted her story to Mike he shivered. "She must have been a very strong woman, both physically and mentally to have survived that," he remarked with admiration. "Just imagine having to feed and water animals in winter on those isolated snow covered hills," he shuddered.

"Yes Rob was in awe of her too," I laughed remembering how I used to tease him about her. "He was very disappointed that she had moved house. He would really have loved to have met her. But she had relocated to a nearby village by the time we were there. She was getting older, and the area was becoming more isolated as her neighbours died, or moved away to live a less challenging life."

"Have you done much walking Rachael?" Mike asked as Carol and Tara came up to join us.

"As much as time allows," I replied moving on to admire a beautiful oleander. "I love long-distance hikes. I love the adventure of it; setting out each morning not knowing where the night will find me. It's totally exhilarating."

Mike and Carol looked at one another and beamed. Mike seemed just about to say something when Liz called out to them to come and join her. I knew from her position what she had found. I too had thought of them when I had passed the water feature earlier. It consisted of a simple grey stone basin, containing a blue and green boat with a man and a woman on board. When the water cascaded down it caused the boat to travel around the circumference of the bowl.

While Carol and Mike joined Liz, Tara and I went to sit in the sunshine on the west facing patio. Hanging baskets laden with petunias, trailing ivy, and orange and yellow nasturtiums adorned the walls, together with colourful tiles which Rose had obviously gathered as souvenirs over years of travelling. Mementoes from Rome, Sicily, Majorca, Venice, Florence, Nice, Antibes, Burgos, Paris, Barcelona made up this colourful terracotta photo album in the centre of which a vibrantly coloured wall hanging proclaimed; "Man is closer to God in a garden than anywhere else on earth."

From my vantage point on the veranda I could observe the other members of the group.

David followed Rose, Pied Piper like, around the garden stopping at various plants and flowers, asking how to germinate, when to take cuttings, when to prune, when to plant, how to care for. He was clean-shaven and well groomed. His clothes fit him perfectly and were spotless. I was very interested to know if he had had any success in tracing Mary, but hadn't had the opportunity to ask him yet. However his demeanour certainly didn't suggest that he was depressed in any way.

Judging by her appearance Liz had also clearly benefited from the course. She had lost that frazzled look and was dressed in calming blue. Carol and Mike were more tanned and toned than when I had last seen them. Sandra seemed relaxed and comfortable in the company. And Rose appeared happy. For some reason the phrase, "In the world, but not of the world," came to mind. She just seemed so at peace with everything and everyone.

I found myself thinking that it would have been interesting if Tara had taken a photograph of us on the first night of the course, and then again on that night in the garden, a kind of before and after exercise. But that would only have told half the story. In my case, and I was sure in the case of all the others, the real change had happened on the inside, and had been gradual, practically imperceptible. It was only when I took the time to try to remember how I was feeling in the bad days that the extent of my improvement was obvious to me.

When the whole group was assembled on the patio Rose opened the glass doors which gave access to the sun room. The strains of Handel's "The Arrival of the Queen of Sheba" wafted out. I recognised it immediately. It was a piece I frequently played when trying to access the vibrations of genius. Then the aroma of freshly baked bread, herbs and spices, filled the air as Rose and Liz placed platters of piazzas, colourful salads, homemade breads, scones, and fruit preserves on a trellis table which ran along the side of the veranda. Refusing any offers of help they returned to the kitchen and came back carrying large pitchers of fruit juices.

"The drink in the floral jugs has just a hint of something," Rose smiled. "It's for the non-drivers." She didn't identify the something.

"Please help yourselves," she urged handing us each a very colourful plate on which the words; thanks, love, energy and home cooking, were written in vibrant colours. "A local potter made them for me," she replied when I asked where she had purchased them. "I'll give you his number."

Then a chorus of voices made it clear that I wasn't the only one interested in the "good vibrations" dishes. Rose nodded and smiled as we all tucked into the delicious food.

When dusk descended shafts of light gleamed from under bushes, and from nooks and crannies in the walls and rockery. For an instant I was reminded of a scene from a science fiction movie as delicate rainbows of light illuminated the darkness.

"Aren't they wonderful?" Rose asked when Liz commented on them. "I just love the multicoloured ones. I think they're amazing."

"They demonstrate the power of sunlight to recharge batteries, ours included," Tara said with a smile.

In the cool of the evening we moved inside. Brightly coloured cushions were scattered on the furniture which was upholstered in a vivid floral material, and the beautiful perfume of roses wafted from an oil burner on the hearth. Tara sat on the settee beside Liz and I sat beside her. Carol and Sandra smiled at us from across the room. Mike and David followed Rose into the sitting room and came back carrying a chair each, which they placed in such a way as to form a circle.

The move in from the garden seemed to add an intimacy to the gathering. Initially the conversations were between people who were seated in close proximity. In response to Tara's question, as to how the children were, I heard Liz reply that, thanks to Rose's parenting tips, things had improved immensely.

"In fact I realised that the children were fine. I was the one needing help. I just wasn't handling them properly," she confessed. "I was constantly giving out to them. The only time I gave them any attention was when they were misbehaving. When they were behaving properly I never thought of praising them. So it was only logical that they would play up in order to get the attention they were seeking. And I was always telling them what not to do, instead of emphasising what they could do. But as soon as Rose advised me to remember "not to think of an elephant," I stopped my negative programming."

"What do you mean not to think of an elephant?" Tara asked.

"If I say to you, "Don't think of an elephant," what immediately comes to mind?"

"An elephant," Tara laughed.

"That's what happens when we constantly tell children what not to do. We are actually planting the idea in their heads. Stressing what they can do is much more productive."

At that point the mumble of voices seemed to stop simultaneously. In the relative quiet David was the only one still speaking.

"The first night was my turning point," he remarked to Mike. Then aware that everyone had heard him he continued without any apparent sense of self-consciousness. Rather, he raised his voice to include us all in the conversation.

"My birthday was the week before the course started," he continued. "The thought of another birthday coming hadn't bothered me at all. But when the day actually arrived, and when I woke up and looked around the room where I was sleeping, I felt disgusted. There were heaps of old clothes everywhere. The floor and bedside table were covered with dirty cups. Broken drawers with clothes spilling out of them hung out of the presses. The curtain rails were falling down, and the curtains were filthy.

It had been like that for ages, but somehow that morning it seemed worse. I was sixty years old and I lived in a dump. I had turned my mother's house into a tip. My father was right after all. I was a no-good who would never be any good. I was a mess. I was alone, an alcoholic, a useless individual. I felt that I wanted to die. But there was no point in thinking like that. I would probably make a mess of that too. After all I could do nothing right. My father had told me so. This then was to be my existence for the rest of my days. When that thought struck me I covered my head and sank down deeper under the bedclothes. Eventually, when the hunger drove me to the kitchen, I felt even more depressed. The sink was full of dirty dishes. There wasn't a clean cup or glass in the place. There were bags of rubbish and old take-away food cartons everywhere. I was starving. I couldn't remember the last time I had eaten a proper meal. The fridge was empty except for some out of date sausages. I felt so miserable. I just put on my coat and walked to the train station. I had no idea where I was going, but anywhere was better than staying in that house.

I got on the first DART that came along. Due to repair works on the line it stopped at Dalkey where there was a bus waiting to carry the passengers to Dublin. I decided to stay there. It's a lovely village and it reminded me of my mother. She loved going there for lunch.

As I passed Flanery's pub the smell of cooking stopped me in my tracks. I remembered the delicious meals which we had often enjoyed there. So I went in and sat in the first alcove to the left of the door, where we used to sit. When the waitress came I ordered one cottage pie. This was my first time there ordering for one. That realisation hit me very hard. I was alone. Nobody wanted anything to do with me. My father was right. It was my fate to be lonely and miserable. So what was the point in me trying? I was doomed to misery. This was the way it was always going to be, so why was I denying myself the only thing that gave me the chance of escaping, if only for a little while?

When I had finished the first whiskey I ordered another, and then another, and another. I remember stumbling to the station. Then there's a blank.

The next thing I recall is waking up in hospital. I had fallen into the gap between the train and the platform. Luckily the driver saw me and called for help. I wasn't badly hurt, just a few bruises. But that really frightened me. I could have lost my legs, or my life. I knew then that I really had to do something to help myself. If I continued as I was going I would end up dead, and I would never get to see my child or Mary again. I didn't want that to happen. I didn't want to die without trying to make amends. I wanted to clear my conscience. I wanted to ask for forgiveness.

The fright of that night drove me back to the A. A. meetings. Then everything seemed to fall into place. When giving their testimony somebody mentioned that they had found Tara's course very worthwhile. That's how I came to be there. And then on that first night it seemed as if the course was planned especially for me. I couldn't believe how helpful it was. When I realised the power of the little voice in the head I was stunned. Repeating the words; "I'm weak, I'm weak, I'm weak," was normal for me. They were the words, or words like them, which had been constantly playing in my head for as long as I could remember. I knew before Tara touched me that my arm would prove weak. That was the story of my life.

But when I realised the difference which repeating the words; "I'm strong," "I'm strong," "I'm strong" made, I was amazed. For the first time I had hope. I understood that I had control over the way I felt.

Then observing you all as you acted the part of an old person was like looking at myself in the mirror. Your backs were bent and your heads were down, just as mine always was. However by just pretending that you were young and fit, the difference was incredible. You all actually appeared more powerful, vigorous, and energetic. That got me thinking that I could help myself to feel strong, capable and in control by "acting as if." Of course, after so many years of negative programming, I realised that I had a hard struggle ahead of me, but I also knew that the effort would pay off. I had seen it with my own eyes.

But more than anything else, your demonstration of the power of love to heal was the most valuable lesson I have ever learned," he said looking at Tara. "When you asked us to tap into a loving vibration, despite the dreadful state I was in, the memory of my mother made me feel good. When you explained that we could access that vibration permanently by loving ourselves, I was hooked.

Until that night I had no idea what it meant to love myself. I didn't know that it involved treating myself as I would a loved one by making my home and environment as beautiful as possible, and by surrounding myself with good vibrations.

It had never occurred to me before that celebrating my uniqueness was important for my good health. I never imagined that by neglecting to use my talents I was denying energy to my second chakra and leaving myself open to addictive behaviour. That realisation, more than anything else, has helped me out of the darkness." His voice broke as he looked at Tara. Then composing himself he continued, "Thanks to your help and advice I started to paint again, and that has given me so much pleasure and peace. Because of your encouragement I now treat myself in a loving way. For me this has meant making huge changes. As I'm sure was obvious to you all on that first night I was a mess. But when I did as you suggested and cleaned myself up, and with your help de-cluttered my house, my life changed for the better. I now had a space to enjoy my meals, and to paint. I was no longer ashamed to open the door. I wasn't embarrassed to invite people in. I felt freer, happier, and more worthwhile.

Then an amazing thing happened. One sunny morning I got up early and was on the road to Enniscorthy almost before I realised it. When I looked around the lovely, clean, ordered house which thanks to your help I now lived in, I felt that the time was right to try to locate Mary. Now I had no excuse. Before that I had used the state of my home, and my life, as a reason for not seeking her out in earnest. But now, thanks to your practical input my house was in order. And more importantly, because of your moral support and understanding, I reckoned that I couldn't be the useless person I had been brainwashed into believing I was, when normal, lovely people were willing to be my friends. That made me think that perhaps it was possible that Mary and our child would at least give me the opportunity to ask their forgiveness.

If I was to be honest with myself I would have had to admit that the chances of locating Mary, or finding out anything about her by going to Enniscorthy were zilch. In fact it was like looking for a needle in the proverbial haystack. But it made me feel good. At long last I was doing something constructive, something positive to try to make amends. After that first trip I came home, studied the map, and decided on a course of action which I felt might produce results. I drew a circle which enclosed every village within a ten mile radius of the town. My original idea was to go the local post office and enquire if there was a family of Kilkolms living in the area. But when I did this I found that the postmaster, or mistress, would ask the name of the person I wanted to find, their father's name, and how long they had been living in that village. When I couldn't answer any of these questions they looked warily at me.

After a few of these experiences I decided this was never going to find her. Worse than that, it could prove dangerous. I was sure that my conversation would be repeated to all the locals who came into the post office, and that it could raise suspicions. That was the last thing I wanted to happen. I didn't want to expose Mary's life to curiosity.

So after that, on my trips to Enniscorthy, I just drove around getting the feel of the place. I somehow felt close to her there. On occasions I'd have my lunch in a small pub in a tiny village and have a chat with the barman, or get into conversation with some of the locals about Wexford's chances in the hurling final. Other times I'd just sit in the car in a nice quiet place and read the papers as I ate my packed lunch. Sometimes I'd take out my sketch pad and outline anything I felt I would like to paint.

That's what I did two Sundays ago. I parked outside the walls of a beautiful old church, and when I had eaten my lunch I took out my jotter and sat on the wall to draw it. Then before driving home I decided to take a stroll in the tiny graveyard. It was beautifully kept. Although many of the graves were very old, some dating from the 1860s, there were fresh flowers and newly planted shrubs on many of them. There was a magnificent Celtic cross erected to the memory of a Father Michael Molloy, who had ministered in Coillcrone from 1828-1860. Judging from the size and design of the memorial he was well-loved and fondly remembered. I thought that perhaps he was another hero like Father Murphy, whose grave I had come across the previous week in the nearby village of Boolavogue. While, from the dates on this headstone, it was clear that Father Molloy had not led his parishioners in the 1798 rebellion as Father Murphy had done, it was possible that he too was a champion of the people. Maybe he had helped to feed and support them during the great famine of 1847-1849, when half the population of the country had died of starvation.

As I said the cross was decorated with beautiful intricate Celtic designs, and I made a rubbing of them before sitting on the little seat which faced the sun. I was the only person in the graveyard so I closed my eyes, and breathing deeply I imagined filling myself with the peace of the place, smiling it into every organ of my body. When I felt nice and relaxed I got up and started back to the car reading the dedications on the headstones as I walked along. All the famous Wexford names were there; White, Murphy, Doyle, Furlong, Walsh, Rossiter, Kilkolm. I couldn't believe it Kilkolm. Kilkolm; they were Mary's people. It was a family plot, a double grave. There were two headstones side by side; a relatively new granite one, and a simpler much smaller stone. My eyes darted from one to the other and the words of both are implanted in my brain for all time.

The larger stone bore the inscription;

In loving memory of
Saul Kilkolm
1915 -1993
His son John
1952-2000
 lost at sea
Ar dheis Dé go raibh a nanamacha dílse.

On the smaller stone I read;
Here lies
David Kilkolm
Adored son and grandson
1973 aged three months.

Horror overcame me. I realised that this could be my son's grave. I wanted to scream but I could hardly breathe. I looked around in panic. I was all alone there. I didn't know what to do. I didn't know where to turn. I wasn't prepared for this. It had never occurred to me that something like this could happen. I hadn't really thought of how it was going to affect me to get any news of Mary, but I never, ever, foresaw anything like this.

I can't really describe how devastated I felt. I thought my heart was about to explode. My body was under such pressure that I was sure I was going to die.

At different times in my life, when I had hit rock-bottom, I had often thought of ending it all. But that day I didn't want to die. For the first time in years I had begun to feel optimistic about my life. My house was in order. I had started to paint again, and I had the company of the group. When this thought flashed through my mind I recalled the advice which Tara had given about handling stress, and so I consciously told myself to be calm, and repeated the word over and over. Then, lying down flat on the ground, I relaxed into the earth and tried to breathe slowly and deeply. I have no idea how long I stayed there, but it seemed like a very long time before my body stopped shaking. When I eventually sat up my head was bursting. I could almost hear Tara telling me to drink some water. I knew there was still tea in my flask in the car, but I didn't have the strength to make it back there. Then I noticed the little tap on the wall of the cemetery. Very slowly I got to my feet, and using the headstones as crutches, I made my way to it. The first few gulped mouthfuls caused me to retch, but when I sipped it slowly, it stayed down.

Then sitting on the wall I wondered how I was ever going to get back to Bray. Once again the group came to mind. I realised that I wasn't totally alone. I had friends who would help. That thought gave me the strength to drive home. Then I went immediately to see Tara and told her what had happened.

Early the next morning, in the Registrar's Office, we found little David Kilkolm's birth certificate. He was not my child. But he was someone's. Someone in that little village is still mourning their precious baby, and I owe them a debt of gratitude.

My experience reminded me that time is very valuable, and life is fragile and precious. So I decided there and then to start searching in earnest. Tara helped me to join Facebook where I posted a request to befriend all the Kilkolms, born in 1972 or 1973, with a view to exploring our family tree.

Last week I got a reply. There was no information given, just an "info @business" address. It acknowledged the query and asked for some time to respond.

It's just like a pregnancy. I don't know whether I have a boy or a girl, but that's not important. My child is alive, that's the most important thing. Hopefully I will have the opportunity to make amends in some way. And I intend to keep myself well so that I won't let him, or her, down a second time. It's not easy, but I don't ever want to go back to that dark place again."

"Carol and I believe that it was the magic of water which guided us to the course," Mike said as soon as David had finished speaking. "As you all know we have always loved the sea. From the time we were children we dreamed of sailing around the world. Six years ago my business was doing well and we thought we had it made. We had the boat. We had money in the bank. We gave ourselves another two years, just to wind the business down and to give the men time to find other employment. Then we planned to up sticks and sail away to live the dream. And this dream was even better than the one we had as kids. This time we wouldn't need to work for anyone else. We'd have enough money to fund ourselves. We had it all planned. We knew the ports we were going to visit; San Sebastian in Northern Spain, Port de Soller in Mallorca, Puerto de Mogan in Gran Canaria, St. Raphael and St Tropez in France, and Cefalu in Sicily. It was a dream list.

And then our world disintegrated. The building industry collapsed and took my business with it. It was unbelievable how quickly it happened. Initially I thought it was just a blip and that things would pick up again. So I kept the men on. Many of them had served their apprenticeship with me. I knew their wives and families. I didn't want to let them go. They were good people. I knew that losing their jobs would devastate them.

But when the recession continued, I had no choice. I had to make them redundant. There was no work, even for myself. It was horrific. Practically overnight a lifetime's labour disappeared. We were destroyed, although we hadn't done anything wrong. We hadn't borrowed huge sums of money to speculate on property. We hadn't bought apartments abroad with money we were trying to hide from the tax man. We had just been too trusting, and had supplied developers who now refused to pay us. It was very soul-destroying, especially since they didn't seem to have suffered any change in their circumstances. They were still living in luxurious accommodation which they said belonged to their wives or children. They still golfed in Spain and Portugal living the high life far-removed from the people they were hurting, whereas I was meeting my creditors every day on the street. That was the hardest part for me; owing money to small subcontractors who had supplied me with goods and services on trust. I couldn't do that to them. I couldn't hold up my head in the town if I let them down, so we took out the money we had saved for our trip, sold the boat and the car and all Carol's jewellery, except her wedding ring. We even put the television, computers, micro wave cooker, electric clothes drier and dish washer on eBay.

On the first night of the course we were hurting very badly. We had just signed a contract to rent our home and were moving into a granny flat in our son's house. You can't imagine how humiliated, useless, and ashamed I felt. And I was so sad for Carol who was now handing over the beautiful home she had made to strangers.

The only thing which kept us sane during that time was the enjoyment we got from the sea. Every night we walked down to the harbour to feed the swans, or to fish off the pier. I hadn't done that in over twenty years; not since I'd started working. Now I realised again what a rich source of food the sea was. We thanked God on many occasions for the fish which I caught for our dinner.

Our lives revolved around the sailing club. We spent all our days there. It gave us a focus; a reason to get up. The people there were our friends. We could just have a chat and a very enjoyable evening with like-minded folk, without spending any money. They didn't treat us any differently, or make us feel pitiful. Indeed many of them were suffering too. Many were trying to help their children who had borrowed large sums of money for houses at the height of the boom, and were now unemployed and struggling to pay huge mortgages.

It was also thanks to the sailing club that we discovered Tara. One day from the terrace I noticed a very colourful lady sitting cross-legged on the sand, and even though I was some distance away from her I could sense her peace. When I enquired about her I was told her name was Tara. After that I noticed her ad. for the Good Vibrations Course in various locations around the town. It sounded as if it was just what we needed, and it was.

The night we learned of the healing vibrations of water put a totally new perspective on our situation. If you remember the most beautiful crystals were formed when the words; health, thanks, friends, love, mum, dad, family, home cooking, were placed near the water. We then realised that we had all those things. That lifted us. Up to that point we were still concentrating on the losses we had suffered. That night we realised how lucky we were and how much we had to be grateful for.

After that we were even more thankful to the water. We sent it good vibrations with gusto and unbelievable things started to happen. Jack, the sailing club manager asked me to help out in the bar. Then the chef got ill and he asked if Carol would be interested in doing the catering. He knew from coming to our house for the occasional dinner party that she was a great cook. Carol was thrilled to get the work. Thinking of what Tara had advised she used only the most colourful and freshest foods, as near to their natural state as possible. She blessed everything that left the kitchen and everyone who would eat it. Then a fortnight ago, during the sailing festival, we hosted clubs from Wicklow and Dublin. On the Saturday when lunch was over and the dining room was quiet, Jack came into the kitchen and announced that a guest wanted to meet the chef."

He stopped there and motioned to Carol who continued with the story.

"I didn't know what to expect," she said. "It had been a very busy lunch, and while I knew that I had cooked with as much care as possible, I was a little apprehensive. When I went into the dining room a young man introduced himself as Kenneth Burke, shook my hand and congratulated me on my cooking. Then he invited me to go out onto the balcony with him."

"That's my yacht," he said pointing to the biggest boat in the harbour. She was called *Uisce Beatha*. (The Water of Life).

"Oh she's so beautiful," I said. "You'd have no trouble going anywhere you wanted to in a boat like that."

"And if you had a boat like that where would you like to go Carol?" he asked.

"I'd love to sail away to the sun for a little while and forget all my land-locked problems," I said.

"Done," he replied immediately.

While I stood there looking at him with my mouth open, he explained that he needed a cook for a six month stint as he cruised the Mediterranean. He said that my cuisine was exactly what he wanted; colourful, unadulterated, fresh, healthy and delicious.

"But I have ties" I said. "I wouldn't leave my husband."

"And what if I made you an offer that you couldn't refuse?" he asked.

"Even then," I said. "I wouldn't go without my husband."

Then he said how sorry he was to hear that. But that he couldn't offer to take my husband on board unless he was an experienced sailor, with a great knowledge of boats, engines, and navigation. He said this laughingly, completely unaware that he had just described Mike.

A short time later it was settled. We are now going to see the world in a much better yacht than we could ever have afforded, courtesy of a dot-com millionaire. Our wish has been granted. The water has repaid our good vibrations. We'll be living the dream and still saving all the money we earn. It will help us get back on our feet again, and Mike won't have the responsibility of running a business. For the first time in many years we will be carefree and doing something we love to do. It's strange, what we considered a disaster may well prove to be not so disastrous after all. Perhaps, because we've always loved the water and been thankful for all the pleasure it has given us, perhaps those good vibrations are coming back to us. It certainly seems like it. In our case the sea is a life-saver. We'd be sunk without it," she smiled.

Sandra was the next person to speak.

"Sean didn't want to come to the course. But I nagged and nagged him. I even drove him here to ensure that he'd attend. That will show you how against it he was, and how determined I was to change his mind. But from the very first night, when he came home and threw the course notes on the table declaring it a load of airy-fairy nonsense, he became more and more negative about it. Eventually his grumbling wore me down and I gave up trying to persuade him to come. There was no point. But I learned a very valuable lesson from that experience. I learned that I can't change anyone unless they want to change and that I shouldn't let anyone or anything change me unless I want to be changed. That's what I had done. I had let Sean's trauma change me. For the past two years, since those men broke into the shop and left him for dead, my life and the children's lives have changed completely. Before his ordeal Sean was an outgoing, confident, happy person: always laughing and singing along to the radio. After it he was a nervous wreck. He was afraid of everything, of sudden noises, of people approaching us on the street, of going into buildings. It was horrendous. He practically barricaded us into the silent house. We tiptoed around and spoke in whispers for fear of upsetting him. I had to stop working. I couldn't continue dressmaking because the idea of people coming to the house disturbed him. And I was so concerned about him that I didn't even consider the effect that was having on me and the children. I found the whole thing practically unbearable. Life was a constant drudge. I was trying to survive on very little money and I was also missing the contact with other people. That's why I begged Sean to come to the course. I felt that he needed good vibrations to get him out of the deep dark hole he was in. But I was wrong, and I was so disappointed.

Then I decided that if he wasn't going to come that I would. I honestly didn't care whether it was going to help me or not. At least it would give me a break from the house and the depressing atmosphere there and I would get to meet other people. So in preparation I read the notes of the first few sessions. They were a revelation. Up to that point I had thought that it would be selfish of me to have any enjoyment in my life while Sean was so miserable. But the notes said that it was my duty to love myself and to provide myself with the things that made me happy. That realisation helped enormously. The next morning as soon as I got up, instead of sneaking around in silence, I turned on the radio. Kris Kristofferson was belting out; "Getting by, High, and Strange." I remembered singing that song at a karaoke competition on our honeymoon. I brought the house down, not because I was so good, but because I was so bad. However I did get a special commendation for my playing of the air guitar.

That memory made me smile. For the first morning in a long time I called the children for school with a smile on my face.

And secure in the knowledge that I wasn't being selfish by doing the things that pleased me I started to work again. That has helped me enormously. When I had to give it up I was full of hatred for the people who were responsible for our misery. But now I try not to think about them. Filling myself with hatred does not affect them in any way, but it could leech all the pleasure from my life. So now I've decided to try as best I can to live my life as I would have done if this hadn't happened. I believe that is the best way for my family's sake, Sean included. Being down and depressed and unhappy in sympathy with him for the past two years hasn't worked. So now I'm going to change tactics completely. I'm going to give the course strategies a try. I'm going to be positive. It's much easier said than done. Because we have spent so much time being negative I have to read the course notes every day to remind me of what I should do. For me singing along to the radio lifts my mood immediately. And the children and I massage one another's feet. We enjoy that immensely.

Oh there are still days when I have to drag myself out of bed. But I know that staying there would achieve nothing, besides the children would be in jumping on top of me," she laughed. "I just hope that by staying positive and by performing the strategies every day, that I will be able to manage, and that perhaps Sean will be encouraged to do likewise. But he is a grown man. I must let him work his way through this in whatever way he sees fit."

"I never had any intention of coming to the course," Liz said. "In fact I had forgotten all about it. I had only agreed to come in the first place to please Frank. I'd have agreed to anything the night he suggested it. He was so angry when he came home to find me, once again, still in my dressing gown in a chaotic kitchen screaming at the children. There was no dinner cooked and no shopping done.

He just turned around, went out, and came back with burgers and chips for the tea, and the course flyer which he said was on the counter in The Tea Cup. When he suggested that I should attend it, I agreed. It was a week away. I was sure he'd forget. But he didn't.

Half an hour before it was due to start he woke me up. I had fallen asleep on the settee, as was normal for me. Every time I sat down I fell asleep. When he called me to go I said I didn't have the energy. Then he became very angry, shouting about how hard he found it to come home at night to a messy house, with no dinner ready, no shopping done, the children going wild, and me always complaining about being tired. I had never seen him so annoyed before. That's why, if you remember, I was very upset. I was afraid that he would leave me. That was the only reason I came. I didn't believe that it would help me. I thought nothing could. I had had a cancer scare, and although the doctor assured me that the cyst was pre-cancerous I was at my wit's end. I couldn't stop worrying about it. I spent so many sleepless nights lying awake in terror, wondering if I was more likely than most to develop cancer.

I couldn't sleep with the anxiety, and then during the day I felt so exhausted that I couldn't function properly. Even the simple things like taking a walk, or going shopping, drained me physically. And that added to my health concerns. I wondered if I was tired because there were more pre-cancerous cells in my body waiting to develop. There appeared to be nothing that I could do to make things better. My life seemed to have been taken from me. It was as if my body was in control and I was just a passenger at its mercy, just a very frightened onlooker. It could decide whether to develop cancer or not.

And I thought Frank was very insensitive to insist that I attend. I thought that he didn't appreciate how low I was feeling, and what the cancer scare had taken out of me. I felt that he wasn't empathising with me and didn't appreciate how sick I was of tests and doctors and hospitals. That he didn't understand how vulnerable I was feeling, not knowing how to make things better. That was the worst thing for me, the feeling of helplessness.

But when I became aware of the research carried out by Dr. Warburg, which proves that proper breathing is a very effective weapon against cancer and low energy, I had hope. Hope that I could avert the cancer. I now knew that I had power. A winner of the Nobel Prize for medicine had proven that I could influence my life and my health.

From then on I became aware of my breathing at all times. I breathed deeply at the traffic lights, when waiting in a queue for the bus, or at the checkout in the supermarket. I read somewhere that our lives are measured, not in years, but in the number of breaths we take, so I resolved to make the most of each one.

After a few weeks I began to notice a change in my attitude. I felt more positive. Previously I had just wanted to sit in a corner and do nothing. That's why the children were so out of control. I had fed all my energy to my worry, and had none left for them. From the time they got up in the morning till they went to bed at night it was like a battlefield. I found it all so relentless; getting them out to school, then cooking dinner, helping with homework, preparing lunches, and in between times refereeing battles. It exhausted me.

But now I find that I can get through the day. At the moment that is the situation, I manage to get through the day, which is a huge improvement on three months ago. And my world is definitely more beautiful. I make a conscious effort to allow only positive things into my life. I spend time outdoors and am very discerning about the television programmes I watch and about the amount of time I am exposed to magnetic rays. I use essential oils in my bath, and put a few drops on dishes in the sun on the window-sills. I add some to the rinsing water for my underwear and bed clothes. I wear the perfume Frank bought me when we were going out together; "Coco" by Chanel. And every time I put it on, it reminds me of how happy I was that he loved me. It makes me smile, and I then fill my body with that happy, loving feeling.

Recently Frank has started to remark on how well I look. I think the bright colours that I'm now wearing are responsible for that. And thanks to Rose's hints I am also conserving my energy when dealing with the children. When she first suggested that I play with them I dismissed the idea completely. But I have found that just sitting down on the floor with them, and being there physically, is all they want. I don't have to do a thing. In fact the less I do the better. This is their time to play, experiment, fantasise and be in control. They choose whatever they wish to play with, and they are the play masters. I just comment and praise. It is fun, and more energy saving than roaring at them from a great height.

And before we go anywhere we draw out a picture schedule of what is going to happen. So for example, before going to the supermarket, which was generally a nightmare with the children running up and down the aisles, we draw pictures of us arriving there in the car, of them walking beside me, helping me to get things out of the fridge and off the shelves, and of the treat they will get for behaving properly.

Like everything I know it will take a little while to work perfectly but already there is a change in their behaviour. And my life has definitely improved. I am better able to cope.

When Liz stopped speaking I realised that if the order was to continue, it was now my turn to tell my story. I didn't feel panicked or even the slightest bit anxious. Everyone else had just spoken from the heart and I did the same.

"My twin sister died and I was distraught," I began. "Anytime I thought of her or heard her name mentioned, I experienced a panic attack. These attacks were very severe and affected me deeply, leaving me exhausted for the next few days. But that wasn't the worst part. They robbed me of my confidence and left me feeling unsure and very vulnerable. I had experienced similar attacks many years previously," I told them, recalling an incident which had lain buried in my memory for a long time. I hadn't thought about the Oakwood Secondary School for Girls for many years. But now it came to mind very clearly, and I informed the group that it was there where I had first experienced fear, panic, and dread.

"My parents were so proud of me when I won a scholarship to one of the countries most exclusive fee paying schools," I continued. "But from the moment I set foot inside the front door I realised that I was in an alien environment. While the intention of the board in awarding such a scholarship may have been prompted by a desire to help less privileged children, many of the people who worked there were sadly lacking in basic human kindness. From the start it was made very clear to me that I was not considered as equal to my classmates. I was there on sufferance.

It was also glaringly obvious that there was a huge difference between my lifestyle, and that of the other children in my class. The summer before my admittance I had spent my holidays in our friend's house in Bray, while most of my new classmates had holidayed in France, or Spain, or Italy. Many had their own ponies and were chauffeured to school, while I travelled on my bicycle. That, and my very obviously second-hand uniform, marked me out as different from the start.

Coming from the primary school, where I had experienced only affection and encouragement, the Oakwood Secondary School for Girls was, for me, a complete and total nightmare. There were times when some of the teachers made very thinly veiled comments aimed at me. If there was graffiti on the wall, or if something was broken in the bathroom, they would suggest that it was as a result of letting children who weren't used to the "finer things in life" into their school. Generally, I was able to cope with the strong feelings of embarrassment and fear which I felt on these occasions. I found that by intertwining my fingers as tightly as possible, and by giving them my full concentration, I could block out whatever was being said.

My parents were completely unaware of the torture I was suffering. I didn't want to upset them. My friend Rob was the only person who knew. He often made me laugh plotting his revenge on Miss Adams, the Principal. On many occasions I had to beg him not to let the air out of her tyres when her car was parked in front of Byrne's Shop in the village. I was afraid that, if caught, he'd get into serious trouble. But of course, I had no control over him when I wasn't with him. And I knew with absolute certainty, and a great deal of pleasure, that he was playing knick knack on her door at every opportunity. The thought of her being tormented by Rob, knocking on her door and running away, delighted me.

However, just a week short of my third month in Oakwood, the final straw broke my silence at home and I was released from torture. In the music hall on that Wednesday morning, 22nd November 1995, a day I will never forget, we, the choir, were practising for a Christmas recital of The Messiah when Aysha discovered that the gold watch, which her father had bought her in Dubai, was missing.

Miss Adams was called in. She gave a lecture on the evils of stealing and threatened that if the watch wasn't found she would have to alert the guards. Then before leaving the room she asked me to take my bag and to accompany her to the office. For a moment I didn't understand why. Then it struck me! She thought that I had stolen the watch. Looking around it seemed as if all the girls were staring accusingly at me. I felt devastated and so alone.

Panic overcame me. I couldn't breathe. The more I struggled for breath the more the panic grew. My heart thumped so loudly it frightened me. I was drowning in distress. Unable to breathe, and frightened by the strange sensations which were attacking my body, I gasped for air. The room was spinning. The accusing faces were distorted and terrifying. When the anxiety became too much to bear I just surrendered to it. Somewhere in the distance I could hear Mrs. Hayes, the music teacher, telling me to relax and to breathe slowly. When I came to she was holding a brown paper bag over my nose and mouth. My breathing returned to normal, just as the housekeeper arrived with Aysha's watch which she had found in her dormitory."

Retelling the story, sixteen years later in the company of friends, I could still recall how frightened and devastated I had felt in that alien environment.

"So from then on I couldn't listen to classical music because it reminded me of that horrible place. Well not until the programme on sound," I added saying that until then it had never occurred to me that sound could energise the brain, although I should have realised it sooner, because every time I played "Satisfaction" I felt an immediate energy boost.

"And something else on that programme has helped change my life," I said knowing how dramatic that sounded, but the fact was that it had been dramatic for me. As soon as the presenter had said, "The word is God," it was as if a light had gone on in my brain. I knew it wasn't the first time that this sentiment had been expressed during the course. Indeed there was hardly a session when the power of the word hadn't been alluded to. But that night it struck me very forcibly. And at this point I articulated to the group the reasoning process which had gone on in my head. "If the word is God, I thought, then it has the power to create, so every word I think or speak is creating my reality. Because of this realisation I've tried to keep my spoken and unspoken words positive. It's not easy," I confessed admitting that I hadn't realised how much moaning and complaining I did until I became vigilant.

And finally I added what I had learned from my dealings with Helen.

"Since starting the course I have tried to look on others with gentleness and compassion," I said, "and have found that in doing this I have actually benefited myself,"

"When Peter died a part of me died too," Rose said when I had finished speaking. "I know that's true for anyone who loses a loved one, but most people are better equipped to handle their loss than I was. I was spoiled. Peter did everything. His life was spent making mine as easy as possible for me. I didn't have to worry about managing the money, or checking the bank statements, or paying the bills, or organising the health, car, or house insurance, or booking flights or holidays. My wish was his command.

When he passed, the ordinary everyday things which people have to do assumed enormous proportions, and I was scared. I didn't know how to manage and I was all alone and afraid. I was ashamed to admit to anyone how inadequate I was, and was too proud to ask for help. So I just let everything go. I had no interest in anything. I didn't turn on the television. I didn't meet friends. They were our friends, not my friends. I took to staying in bed for the most part of the day. I just wanted to sleep and sleep and sleep. But no matter how long I slept for, I was still exhausted,

When my daughter would ring from Spain asking me over I pretended that I was fine, and was keeping busy, meeting friends, etc. Then I would promise myself to get up early the next morning, and sometimes I did, but I was no sooner out of bed than I was back in it again. I can safely say that for many weeks the only colour I saw was black. That was the colour of the inside of my eyelids. I don't know what would have happened to me had I not met Tara.

On one of the very rare occasions when I went down the town I bumped into Anne, my neighbour, and we went to The Tea Cup for a cup of coffee. We were sitting in the window-seat, when a girl whom I had never seen before smiled and waved enthusiastically at us. I knew I hadn't seen her before because once seen never forgotten. She was as colourful as a rainbow. When she came inside every pair of eyes in the restaurant was on her. It made me feel good just to look at her.

"She's my new tenant," Anne said when I asked who she was. "She's an energy therapist."

Needless to say it was Tara.

I had forgotten all about that meeting until Sarah rang and said that she and the children were coming to visit in September. I was frantic. I didn't want her to see me the way I was. I looked dreadful. She'd have been so worried. I knew that I had to do something to boost myself. Then I remembered Tara and how wonderful she looked. She was living proof of the wisdom of Jack Bouvier's advice to his daughter Jacqueline. "Fine feathers make fine birds," he reputedly told the woman who went on to marry two of the most powerful men of her time; the American President, John Fitzgerald Kennedy, and the Greek shipping mogul, Aristotle Onassis.

Looking at me then you would never have guessed that I had ever heard that expression, never mind been a firm believer in it. At that time it was so obvious from my dull, dowdy garb that I couldn't care less. No one would have believed that I was once feisty and fun and loved adventure; that I'd been stalked in Sicily, had inadvertently landed on a Mediterranean island nudist colony, had been robbed on the underground in Rome, had narrowly escaped being kidnapped on a camel in Egypt, had travelled from Le Havre, in north western France, to Nice on the Cote D'Azur in a long-distance lorry, communicating with the driver only in the language of smiles.

We had so many great plans for our retirement, Peter and I. We were so happy and thankful to have reached that period in our lives when we had the time and resources to do all the fun things we had been looking forward to. I finally got the sun room which I'd always wanted, and Peter had the garden properly landscaped. He had visions of growing our own fruit and vegetables, looking forward particularly to experimenting with training apple, pear, and plum trees up the garden wall, something which he'd seen done to great effect in an old Victorian walled garden. We also intended studying Italian in Florence, but most of all we were looking forward to spending the winters in northern Spain, close to our daughter Sarah and her family. In that way we'd kill two birds with the one stone. We'd get to know our grandchildren better, and help Sarah and Juan Carlos financially by attending their classes. This was our time to indulge ourselves. At last our children were independent. Sarah's language school had finally become established. During the first few years it had been very difficult for her, and Peter and I had been called on, on quite a few occasions, to help out, but now things seemed to be going well. And John is married in Cork. So we had no worries about them. We were finally free to think about ourselves.

Everything was going well until Peter started to feel uncharacteristically tired. "The only consolation is that pancreatic cancer is very rapid," is how the consultant put it to me. Like so many people hearing that news of a loved one, I would gladly have changed places with him. My motive was a very selfish one. I didn't know how I could ever survive without Peter. He was the substance behind my superficiality, my advisor, my supporter, my admirer. His love allowed me to be carefree, showy, and secure in myself. But much more than that, I loved him deeply and had done since the first moment I had laid eyes on him.

When he passed my life lost its flavour. There was no joy, no fun, nothing to look forward to. But the night Tara spoke about colour and perfume helped me enormously. You see a few weeks previously I had had a very vivid dream in which a young man stood in the sitting room of our home. He was slim and youthful and wore a trilby hat. While I watched he knelt down in front of the fireplace. Then, reaching into the black lifeless cinders, he gently and lovingly lifted out the most perfectly formed, plump, purple heart. Even in my dream its perfume stunned me. Turning, he presented the heart to me. I woke immediately feeling that the dream was a message from Peter. And Tara confirmed that. The purple heart and perfume all have links with the Divine. The dream confirmed what I knew instinctively; that Peter is in a good place. That means everything to me. He is happy. He is in a world of positive vibrations, and to be on his wavelength I have to have colour, perfume, fun, and joy in my life too. That was always his wish for me.

I knew, without the shadow of a doubt, that I had contributed to my illness by cutting off those positive vibrations. So I immediately reintroduced them into my life making it a much more joyful one. I bought seven swatches of material and seven scarves in the rainbow colours, and each day, as well as getting out in the light, I wear a differently coloured scarf, so that in a week I have accessed the whole rainbow and have brought balance into my life. Every day I fill a glass jug with water and leave it outside to absorb the sunshine. I eat the rainbow colours and I also have them in my home. And as you are probably aware I fill my home with the essence of roses. It resonates with my name.

As soon as I opened myself up to the positive vibrations of colour and perfume I started to feel better and this snowballed in a wonderful way. I found that I had the energy and motivation to practise the other strategies also. And then, encouraged by their effectiveness, I took note of everything that you said Tara," she said giving Tara a warm smile, "and found that the things which I needed to hear stayed with me. When you encouraged us to be creative, and to use the talents we have, I started to write, not serious stuff, just recollections of my life in the classroom. It is so therapeutic, such fun, and so rewarding. When it's finished I intend to publish it myself and to use the proceeds to help fund a bus in Peter's memory to take the children in his old school to games and matches. He would love that. You also emphasised the importance of having something to do, so I volunteered to host a phone-in show on the local radio station on Saturday mornings. That will give me a focus and a reason to go on. Thanks to you I am getting my life back. It will never be the same as my life with Peter, but I am starting to see light again and I am so thankful for that."

There was silence in the room for a moment. Then Tara spoke.

"I'm so happy to hear that the course has helped," she said. "But please remember this is now a lifestyle. In order to maintain its benefits it is necessary to keep up the exercises. Don't make the mistake of thinking that once you feel better there is no need to continue with the strategies. Our bodies need love, air, water, colour, perfume, treats, fun, exercise and meditation every day."

"Even you?" Carol asked.

"Of course me," Tara replied laughingly.

"But you're a healer," Carol said. "You're not like the rest of us. You have a special gift."

"I don't have a special gift, Carol. What I do, anyone can do. Indeed it's because I don't have a special gift that the course has come about."

"But you know so much," Carol insisted. "How could you possibly know so much unless you were in some way special?"

"Five years ago I was on top of the world," Tara began. "My life was as close to perfect as I think it is possible to be. I had a lovely home, my parents were very wealthy, I had a wonderful boyfriend, and a job that I loved. Then my father absconded with his secretary and a large sum of company money. The whole family was shamed and under suspicion. I, as the chief accountant, had to explain to the authorities and the shareholders, how I had not been aware of the misappropriation of company funds which, it came to light, had been going on for some time.

Shortly after headlines of the scandal appeared in the National Press my mother died in a car accident which I believe was not unrelated to the stress she was under. So within a few weeks my life, as I had known, it was over. I lost my parents, my boyfriend, my job, and my will to live. I just wanted to die. There was no point in me living. I had nothing to live for. Everything I loved; everything which gave value and meaning to my life had been taken away from me. My existence was aimless. My day was without structure or meaning. There was nothing to look forward to."

While she was speaking I could only imagine how difficult the group was finding it to reconcile the broken person she was describing with the vivacious, colourful woman we had met every Tuesday evening for the past few months. I had had five years to assimilate this information, and there were still times when I looked at Tara and found it difficult to believe that she was once broken and distraught, despite having seen her with my own eyes. There was complete silence in the room as she continued to speak, recounting the dream which she credited with saving her life.

"It is as vivid to me now as it was then, nearly five years ago," she said sitting forward slightly so as to establish eye contact with everyone in the room.

"I dreamed that I was in church and approached the altar rails for communion. But when I looked down I found that the vicar had placed a small brown cross on the palm of my hand. I lifted it to my mouth and put it on my tongue. Then I discovered its true nature. It was not made of wood, as it had appeared to be; rather it consisted of delicious, light, chocolate covered honeycomb. And a gentle voice whispered; "Come to Me all you who labour and are heavy burdened and I will give you rest. For my yoke is sweet, and my burden is light. Love only love is the way."

"Those were the words which were ringing in my ears when I awoke," she said before adding that she could immediately identify the speaker. "For me, the Me being referred to was the Hero of the Bible stories which my grandmother read to me before sleeping," she continued. "It was He who cured the sick; made the blind see, the lame walk, and brought the dead back to life. As a child, listening to those stories, I would close my eyes and imagine Him speaking those exact words to me. "Come to Me. And I will give you rest."

When I awoke from the dream it was as if I had been charged with a bolt of high energy. Even in my semi-conscious state, resulting I now know from malnutrition and dehydration, the quotation delighted me. "Come to Me all you who labour and are heavy burdened and I will give you rest." For the first time in a very long time, there was a purpose to my life, and I felt wanted. "Come to Me," the voice had said. I knew exactly where I was going, and I knew the way to get there. Love was the way.

This message had a profound effect on me because it was not the first time I had heard it," she emphasised looking around the group. "It reiterated a communication which I had received some years previously; a message which I had completely ignored. But this time I was intent on obeying. I realised that it was for my good. I knew that had I

219

listened to it the first time I would not have ended up in the sorry state that I had found myself in.

On waking with those familiar words in my head my immediate, almost instinctive reaction was to recite the prayer which my grandmother had always prayed with me before sleeping; the prayer which Jesus taught. Our Father, Who art in Heaven, Hallowed be Thy name. Thy Kingdom come. Thy will be done on earth as it is in Heaven. Give us this day our daily bread," she prayed stopping there, as she said she had done then, because it was in reciting this line that she was made aware of the importance which Jesus had placed on the care of the body.

"I hope I'm not offending anyone's beliefs," she said scanning the group, "but this is exactly what happened."

Nearly as one we assured her that we were fine with what she was saying, and urged her to continue.

When she spoke again she repeated that Jesus had asked the Father to supply the body's needs before he had requested forgiveness, or even protection from evil. She said it was this realisation which had motivated her to get out of bed and to eat a nutritious meal, something she hadn't done in a number of weeks. She described her concave stomach, how the sagging skin hung loosely from her upper arms, her hollow cheeks, her grey complexion, and her eyes, looking like those of a hunted animal.

She then described how she had gone slowly down the stairs, put some bread in the toaster and an egg on to boil, and immediately set about researching every means possible to nurture the body, and began to incorporate them into her life.

"Was that when you decided to become a therapist?" Liz asked.

"No, I had no intention of becoming a therapist. I just wanted to get well. But the more I returned to health the louder the voice in my head prompted; "You could help others."

"Initially I ignored it. I didn't feel that anyone would be interested in hearing what I had to say. After all who was I to instruct others? I was a party animal, a spoiled, selfish, snobbish individual. I was the last person anyone could take seriously. But the voice refused to listen to reason. The stronger I became, the more it insisted; "You could help others." As my life returned to normal, as my enjoyment of it increased, it continued relentlessly. There was no escaping it. When the media reported incidences of murder, robbery, violence or abuse, it became more resolute; "You have a responsibility. You could make a difference." These words touched a nerve. I found them particularly hard to ignore. They reminded me of the times during my illness when I had asked myself what purpose my life had served; what difference I had made. The answer was a very firm none. And even then, in my deepest despair, the thought that my life had meant nothing troubled me.

As if aware that they had breached a clink in my defence the words became a mantra: "You could make a difference. You could make a difference." Still I continued to resist, until it became obvious that there was no escaping it. And strangely, as soon as I relented and considered the situation calmly, I had to admit that the message made sense, and that the time was right for me to change my career, my location and my lifestyle. For the sake of my health I knew that I needed to cut ties with anything which linked me to the past. So rather than an annoyance I found myself thinking that perhaps the voice was another nudge in the right direction. After all, I reasoned, a similar voice had saved my life and directed me back to good health. Perhaps listening to it again would prove equally beneficial, and would guide me further along the road to health, satisfaction, happiness, and peace. That was when I decided to become a therapist Liz."

"What were the other promptings you refer to?" Carol asked in a tone of genuine interest.

"The deciding factor for me was when in meditation a communication which I had already received was repeated. That was what finally made my mind up. It was then that I decided to become a therapist."

"I'm fascinated," Carol said. "Please go on."

Tara looked around at each of us. "Are you sure I'm not boring you, and that you are too polite to say so?" she asked sincerely.

"Bored," Liz said a look of disbelief on her face; "I'm fascinated, positively fascinated."

"Well if you're sure," Tara continued. We all nodded.

"As I said the deciding factor was when I received a communication in meditation which I had already deliberately ignored. Twelve years previously, in a location literally thousands of miles from here, I had received the same message. That afternoon I had crawled out of bed and had consumed numerous cups of coffee in an effort to dull the pain in my head. It was another "never again day!" The last thing I could remember of the previous evening was sitting on the footpath outside a nightclub, holding my head tightly in my hands to prevent it from bursting. I had left my friends and staggered to the bathroom. Then I had obviously taken a wrong turn and ended up on the street. When the air hit me the effects of the combination of beer, wine and cocktails, which I had drunk, knocked me for six.

I couldn't remember coming back to the apartment. The girls must have brought me home. It wasn't an unusual occurrence. Somehow we felt that our level of intoxication was an indication of how good a time we were having.

When I eventually joined them, at our usual spot on the beach, I gingerly lowered myself onto the empty sunbed beside Sylvia.

"How are you feeling? How's the head?" she asked.

Too drained to speak I responded by sticking out my tongue and adapting a vomit mode.

"I know exactly what you mean. I was afraid to go swimming in case I'd drown. I think I'm still drunk," she laughed.

When I lay down and closed my eyes a wave of nausea overcame me. Inching my way back up into a sitting position I tried to distract myself by observing the other people on the beach. There were children digging in the sand, people swimming, and couples playing a racket and ball game which was very popular there. The sound of the ball hitting against the bat caused every nerve in my body to screech out in pain. Then, whether it was a parent scolding a child, or a man with a large nose, or a toddler with an upturned sun hat, I'm not sure what the trigger was, but suddenly out of the ether the words came loud and clear. "Follow The Maker's instructions." Then bizarrely I had an image of Geppetto, Pinocchio's inventor, warning the puppet to always tell the truth, or his nose would tell the tale. I knew immediately what the message was. I knew it was referring to my lifestyle, but I had no intention of obeying it. I was enjoying partying on the wild side.

However, when those same words were repeated to me in meditation as I was recovering from my illness, they produced a different response from me. Now I was ready to listen. I knew that had I taken heed of them the first time, my life would have been less troubled, and I would have been spared the agony of hitting rock-bottom with its associated devastation. While I couldn't understand why they were being entrusted to me, I felt that I had a responsibility to pass them on to others. After much thought it occurred to me that the only way I could do this was to become a therapist."

"That's so wonderful," Liz enthused. "It's as if you were called. I'm sure many more people would be interested in doing the course if they heard your story. Why don't you advertise this publicly?"

"Because I'm afraid of the ridicule I would be subjected to. I don't want to be considered arrogant, or a crank, or an attention seeker. So I just reveal the strategies which have returned me to good health knowing that by practising them we are obeying The Maker's instructions."

"And what exactly are The Maker's instructions?" Sandra asked.

There was complete silence in the room as Tara answered that question by indicating the search results which, she said, had convinced her that in all traditions, philosophies, and religions there is a common belief that The Maker's instructions are to love the self, others, and creation. She illustrated this point by referencing the Golden Rule which urges us to treat others as we would like to be treated by them. She reminded us that in the Old Testament the instructions given by God to Moses on Mount Sinai are also based on showing love to God, the self and others. In a similar way, she suggested that those who adhere to the Noble Eightfold Path, which in the Buddhist tradition leads to Nirvana, must act in love since it is predicated on compassion. Finally she added that the Christian tradition is also founded on love. The gospels tell us that Jesus preached adherence to two commandments; "Thou shalt love the Lord thy God with thy whole heart, and with thy whole soul, and with thy whole mind. And thou shalt love thy neighbour as thyself."

"You said that had you listened to The Maker's instructions in the first place you would have been spared a lot of hardship, can you explain that please Tara?" Liz asked.

"I firmly believe that had I loved and cared for my body as I should have when my world was disintegrating that I would not have fallen apart. I now know that had I kept myself properly nourished, had I exercised and spent time in the light and stayed positive and in touch with others, I would have been better able to cope. I know that by refusing to eat, and by locking myself in and hiding away, ruminating over my problems, I only made myself ill. All the research points to the fact that for optimum health we must nourish our senses every day with air, water, food, light, sound and touch."

At this stage everyone sat in rapt attention.

Then Rose broke the silence by summarizing what Tara had just said. "So by following The Maker's instructions to love ourselves we will enjoy better health."

"Yes Rose," Tara replied. "As is very clear from the course notes by nourishing our chakras with the positive vibrations of air, light, water, colour, perfume, and laughter, and by exercising and meditating we are provided with all the ingredients which we need to sustain the health of our trinity of body, mind and spirit. In this state we are balanced and happy, and have greater immunity to illness, and no need to overindulge in drugs, alcohol, or food, sparing ourselves the associated diseases and misery."

"You mentioned that the more the news items told of crimes the more the voice in your head insisted that you could help others. Why was this, do you think?" Sandra asked.

"I wondered about that too Sandra," Tara replied. "And then it occurred to me that if there was universal obedience to The Maker's instructions that there would be an end to all crime. Obedience to the Golden Rule and the Commandments would eliminate killing, adultery, stealing, lying, resentment and jealousy. And if we lived by the Noble Eightfold Path and saw the world through the eyes of the Buddha then we would harbour no ill will towards anyone. We would speak only kind and helpful words, and hurt no living creature. We would earn our living in a way that harms no one. We would continually strive to cultivate good qualities in ourselves and try to keep our words and deeds positive. And if we followed Jesus' example and teaching we would spend our lives doing good. If we lived like this the distress and agony which result from crimes against the person would be no more."

Sandra nodded her head in agreement.

"Viewed in this way it is clear that The Maker's instructions are not a series of commands to insure blind obedience, as they are sometimes presented, but rather that they are recommendations issued in the spirit of love which will allow us to resonate with all that is beautiful, good, and healthy," Tara continued. "They are given by a Loving Father for our benefit. His happiness is in no way dependent on our obedience to them, whereas I believe ours is. And just as any maker's intentions are to ensure that the user gets optimum benefit from their creation, so Our Creator, I believe, has given us these instructions to enable us to gain the most from life."

"So the secret to a fulfilled, healthy, and happy life is to follow The Maker's instructions," Liz said.

"Yes, I believe so Liz. I believe that ultimately the only way to gain optimum benefit from life is to love. To love ourselves by eating nutritious foods, by exercising, by maintaining a positive mental outlook, and by engaging in a productive way in society. And to love others by treating them as we would like to be treated by them. I believe that it is only by following The Maker's instructions that we can each reach our full potential."

"Even lame ducks," David whispered good humouredly to Mike, who smiled and nodded enthusiastically.

A smile crossed Tara's lips also as she concluded; "The Bible tells us of the wonderful rewards which will be showered on those who follow the way of love. St. Paul pledges the peace of the Lord which surpasses all understanding. While St. Mathew promises that all other things will be added unto them.

So yes, I believe that to love, simply to love, is the way to follow The Maker's instructions, and to soar."

ACKNOWLEDGEMENT

I will recount all your wonders.
I will rejoice in You and be glad.
And sing songs to Your name O Most High.
         Psalm (9.2-3)